General Certificate Education

GCS Maths

GCSE Maths Practice Papers

(Foundation Tier)

Instructions, Guidance, Practice Papers & Answers

CONTENTS

how2become

As part of this product you have also received FREE access to online tests that will help you to pass GCSE MATHS *Practice Papers (Foundation Tier)*.

To gain access, simply go to:

www.PsychometricTestsOnline.co.uk

Get more products
for passing any test at:

www.how2become.com

Orders: Please contact How2become Ltd, Suite 14, 50 Churchill Square Business Centre, Kings Hill, Kent ME19 4YU.

You can order through Amazon.co.uk under ISBN 9781910602584, via the website www.How2Become.com or through Gardners.com.

ISBN: 9781910602584

First published in 2016 by How2become Ltd.

Copyright © 2016 How2become.

All rights reserved. Apart from any permitted use under UK copyright law, no part of this publication may be reproduced or transmitted in any form or by any means, electronic or mechanical, including photocopying, recording, or any information, storage or retrieval system, without permission in writing from the publisher or under licence from the Copyright Licensing Agency Limited. Further details of such licenses (for reprographic reproduction) may be obtained from the Copyright Licensing Agency Ltd, Saffron House, 6-10 Kirby Street, London EC1N 8TS.

Typeset for How2become Ltd by Anton Pshinka.

Disclaimer

Every effort has been made to ensure that the information contained within this guide is accurate at the time of publication. How2become Ltd are not responsible for anyone failing any part of any selection process as a result of the information contained within this guide. How2become Ltd and their authors cannot accept any responsibility for any errors or omissions within this guide, however caused. No responsibility for loss or damage occasioned by any person acting, or refraining from action, as a result of the material in this publication can be accepted by How2become Ltd.

The information within this guide does not represent the views of any third party service or organisation.

Using your papers

Read the instructions **carefully** before working through the practice papers.

In this book, there are **two** sets of practice papers:

Set A and **Set B**

Each **SET** includes:

➢ **A GCSE Mathematics Formula Sheet**

➢ **Paper 1 – Non-Calculator**   Marks out of 100
*Calculator **NOT** permitted*
1 hour 45 minutes

➢ **Paper 2 – Calculator**   Marks out of 100
*Calculator **IS** permitted*
1 hour 45 minutes

➢ **Answer Booklet**

PLEASE NOTE!

The number of marks and the time limit provided in these practice
papers are for you to use as a **GUIDELINE ONLY**. They do not reflect
the actual duration or the mark scheme of your
Maths GCSE examination.

COMPLETING YOUR PRACTICE PAPERS

In order to complete these practice papers, you will need the following:

➢ GCSE Mathematics Formula Sheet (contained at the beginning of your practice papers)

➢ Pen

➢ Pencil

➢ Eraser

➢ A ruler

➢ A protractor

➢ A pair of compasses

➢ Tracing paper

➢ A calculator (for paper 2 ONLY).

PREPARING FOR YOUR MATHS GCSE

GCSE Maths Is Easy Practice Papers (Foundation Tier) has been specifically designed to complement your classroom and home-based learning, prior to your GCSE Maths examination.

These practice papers should be used to help you revise the content and skills which you have been taught in the classroom. Moreover, these papers will allow you to see which questions you are getting right, and which ones you are getting wrong. This will help you to tailor your revision to your weakest areas, resulting in higher marks overall in your Maths GCSE.

REMEMBER!

Practice *really* does make perfect.

The more you practice, the more marks you will score!

HOW TO WORK THROUGH YOUR PAPERS

In order to make the most out of your practice papers, consider the following:

STEP 1

Undergo one practice exam (one exam consists of both the Calculator and Non-Calculator paper).

STEP 2

Go through your answers and mark your work using the mark scheme provided.

STEP 3

Have a look at what questions you are getting wrong. These are the questions that you need to work on!

STEP 4

Practice these types of question again and then undertake another practice test. If you are still getting those questions wrong, keep practising. Keep revising that subject area until you get them all correct!

STEP 5

Work on **ALL** of your weak areas until you feel confident enough to tackle your GCSE Maths exam with ease.

STEP 6

Be sure to keep testing yourself. Every time you get a question wrong, consider 'why' you got it wrong. Did you understand the question? Did you miscalculate? Did you not know how to work the question out? Work out why you got the question wrong, and learn from your mistakes. Practice these questions thoroughly until you are fully confident enough to tackle and conquer each and every single one!

Calculating your grade

THE IMPORTANCE OF CALCULATING YOUR GRADE

Calculating your grade is an extremely important step in regards to GCSE preparation. By monitoring your performance, you are able to keep track of your progression and determine your strong areas, and more importantly, your weaker areas!

Calculating your grade in practice papers will give you some indication as to what grade or level you are currently working at.

HOW TO WORK OUT YOUR GRADE

The optimal way to monitor your performance is to mark your practice papers as you go.

➢ Once you have completed a whole exam (Calculator and Non-Calculator paper), mark your answers using the mark scheme provided.

➢ All of the papers contained within this guide have a total score of 100. This allows you to easily calculate your percentage.

➢ Mark paper 1 and work out your percentage score. Mark paper 2 and work out your percentage score. Find your average percentage for the whole exam (paper 1 and paper 2).

➢ Using the table below, work out what grade represents your average percentage.

WORKING OUT YOUR AVERAGE %

To work out your average percentage, add up both percentages (for paper 1 and paper 2), and then divide it by 2.

AVERAGE PERCENTAGE AND GRADE

Using your average percentage, work out what grade you achieved.

AVERAGE %	80+	60-79	46-59	28-45	15-27	under 15
GRADE	C	D	E	F	G	U

EXAMPLE

Here is an example of how to work out your average percentage. Say you scored the following in each paper:

➢ *64 marks out of 100 (paper 1: Non-Calculator)*

➢ *76 marks out of 100 (paper 2: Calculator)*

To work out your average:

➢ Because both papers are out of 100, these marks are already in percentages – 64% and 76%.

➢ To work out your average percentage, add up both percentages:

64 + 76 = 140

➢ Now divide it by 2:

140 ÷ 2 = 70.

➢ Using the table above, find which bracket '70' comes under. This is equivalent to a grade D.

RECORDING YOUR SCORES

By keeping a record of your marks/grades in the tables below, you will be able to keep track of your performance.

We recommend that you practice each practice paper **more than once**. That way you should be able to see your results improving.

The saying that *'practice makes perfect'* is spot-on when it comes to preparing for exams. Ultimately, the more you practice, the better your scores will be.

Practice Papers Set A

Write your scores and grades to practice papers A in the table below. We have provided you additional space in case you attempt these papers more than once. This will allow you to monitor your performance and progression.

		Paper 1 %	Paper 2 %	Average %	Grade
Practice Papers A	1st attempt				
	2nd attempt				
	3rd attempt				

Practice Papers Set B

Write your scores and grades to practice papers B in the table below. We have provided you additional space in case you attempt these papers more than once. This will allow you to monitor your performance and progression.

		Paper 1 %	Paper 2 %	Average %	Grade
Practice Papers B	1st attempt				
	2nd attempt				
	3rd attempt				

PLEASE NOTE

The grades you achieve in the practice papers are **NOT** a guarantee of achieving that grade in the real exam. They should merely be used as a guideline in regards to the level you are working at.

UNDERSTANDING THE GRADE BOUNDARIES

Please be aware that this book is for foundation level, and, therefore, the highest grade you can achieve will be a grade C.

This is why the grade box ranges from C-U.

If you were sitting a higher tier paper, you would be able to achieve above a C grade.

This information shouldn't be new to you, and you should have been told what tier paper you will be sitting prior to your examination.

Please be sure that you know which tier paper you will be sitting for your GCSE Maths examination.

Guidance for GCSE

Exams are a stressful time for every student. In the lead up to your exams, it is common for you to be feeling nervous. However, all you need is a survival guide to deal with GCSE examinations in order to aid you during your preparation stages.

STAGE 1 - REVISION

WHEN SHOULD I START REVISING FOR MY GCSES?

You can make your life so much easier by preparing for your GCSEs in advance. By preparing early, you will be able to overcome exam nerves and stress, therefore improving your overall performance when it comes to the real exam.

If you spread your revision out over a prolonged period of time, you:

➢ Will be able to prepare and practice and ultimately improve your performance.

➢ Will reduce the amount of stress that you will be feeling in regards to your exams.

➢ Will be under less pressure and will be able to revise in a more efficient way.

➢ Will still be able to enjoy free time. By not cramming in revision, you will still be able to relax and enjoy yourself.

TOP TIP!

You should begin revising 6-8 weeks prior to your GCSEs. Although you can still achieve high scores if you revise later than this, you won't be able to guarantee your best results.

HOW TO USE YOUR REVISION TIME WISELY

When it comes to exams, the majority of students will have to organise their time sufficiently in order to make the most out of their learning.

Students will likely be facing numerous exams across a short period, and therefore, they need to be able to break up their revision and set aside time for each subject.

Using a timetable can really help you to manage your time wisely.

➢ Work out how many exams you have to revise for.

➢ Factor all of these subjects into consideration, so that you spend a sufficient amount of time on each subject area.

➢ Be sure to make time for breaks and relaxation. You do not want to overload your brain!

➢ Make sure you factor in all your commitments i.e. lessons, social activities, free time, etc.

On the next page, we have provided you with a timetable that you should fill in to help you organise your time. Only you will know what areas you need to work on, so make sure that your timetable reflects this.

REVISION TIMETABLE

Week Beginning: _____

	Monday	Tuesday	Wednesday	Thursday	Friday	Saturday	Sunday
9am							
10am							
11am							
12 noon							
1pm							
2pm							
3pm							
4pm							
5pm							
6pm							
7pm							
8pm							

*You will need to fill in this timetable for every week leading up to your exams. Once you sit an exam, you can take that out of your timetable, and spend more time on something else.

STAGE 2 - THE NIGHT BEFORE YOUR EXAM

NO MORE CRAMMING!

When the night before the exam comes around, you should **STOP** revising. If you continue revising the night before, you will do yourself no favours. You will feel more stressed, more pressured and more tired – none of which will better your performance.

THINGS TO CONSIDER

The night before the exam:

➢ Ensure that you have all of the equipment you need for your exam (pens, pencils, rubbers, protractors, rulers, etc.).

➢ Double check your exam timetable so that you know what the start time is and where the exam is being held.

➢ Have a relaxing bath, and try not to think about the exam.

➢ Try to get an early night. This will allow you to wake up feeling refreshed and ready to go!

STAGE 3 – IN YOUR EXAM

Whilst your brain will be focussed on trying to remember everything you have learned in the last few weeks, there are a few things you need to be aware of.

LISTEN!

An invigilator will start the exam by running through the exam procedures. Pay attention to what the invigilator is saying, as this may answer some of the questions or queries you have about the exam.

When invited to do so, you will need to fill in the front of your examination booklet. The front of your examination paper contains lots of information which you need to read carefully.

INSTRUCTIONS TO CANDIDATES:

➢ Before you begin filling in the front of your examination booklet, make sure that you have the correct testing paper in front of you.

   o Make sure that the paper is for the correct subject (i.e. GCSE Mathematics).

   o Make sure that you are sitting the correct tier (i.e. foundation or higher).

   o Make sure you have all of the papers required for the exam (i.e. Non-Calculator, Calculator, Formula Sheet).

➢ Fill in ALL of your details on the front of your examination booklet. This will usually consist of the following:

   o Surname.

   o First Name/s.

   o Candidate Signature.

   o Candidate Number *(this will be provided to you on the day).*

   o Centre Name and Number *(this will be provided to you on the day).*

➢ Answer **ALL** of the questions in the spaces provided.

➢ When it comes to calculations, make sure you show **ALL** of your workings out.

➢ If you have any questions, please raise your hand and wait for someone to assist.

ACTION CHECKLIST!

➢ Work through the paper at a steady pace.

➢ If you have any questions about the exam, be sure to raise your hand and wait for someone to assist you.

➢ Double-check you have the correct exam paper in front of you.

➢ Make sure you have all of the correct equipment in order to complete the exam.

➢ Don't spend too long on one question.

➢ If you have time at the end, go back through the paper and check your work.

- ➢ Have a bottle of water nearby.

- ➢ Use a watch to monitor your time.

- ➢ Don't panic! You are ready! You are prepared!

STAGE 4 – AFTER YOUR EXAM

AFTER YOUR EXAM, *DO:*

- ➢ Reward yourself with some free time. Even if you have other exams coming up, you should spend some time doing something you enjoy. Just relax!

- ➢ Forget about the exam. It's over. There is no point dwelling about what you could have done, or what you didn't do.

- ➢ Be positive and proud. If you put that extra time and hard work into preparing for your exam, then you have done your best, and that's all you can do.

AFTER YOUR EXAM, *DON'T:*

- ➢ Do a post mortem of your exam. Do not pick your exam apart. Do not think about the 'what ifs'. The exam is over. You cannot change anything now, so try not to worry.

- ➢ Discuss the exam with your friends. Discussing the exam and then thinking 'I didn't write that' or 'I should have done that', will make you feel disheartened. Try to avoid any conversation about the contents of the exam.

- ➢ Worry yourself. Everyone comes out of exams fearing the worst. This is a common feeling amongst students, and chances are, you are worrying over nothing.

- ➢ Feel upset or disheartened if the exam didn't go according to plan. There are several opportunities for re-sits, and who knows, you may have done better than expected!

Prepare! Practice! Persevere!

SURNAME		CENTRE NAME					
FIRST NAME/S		CENTRE NUMBER					
CANDIDATE SIGNATURE		CANDIDATE NUMBER					

GCSE Mathematics

SET A
Paper 1 Non-Calculator

Foundation Tier

1 hour and 45 minutes

INSTRUCTIONS TO CANDIDATES

- Use **black** ink.
- **Fill in the boxes** at the top of this page.
- Answer **all** of the questions.
- **Clearly** show your workings out.

INFORMATION FOR CANDIDATES

- The **total mark** for this paper is **100**.
- The marks for each question are shown on the **right** side of each page.
- Questions labelled with an asterisk (*) will assess the **quality** of **written communication**.

ADVICE FOR CANDIDATES

- Keep a close eye on the **time**.
- **Do not** spend too long on one question.
- Try to answer **every** question and show your workings out when required.

	For examiner's use						
Q	**Attempt No.**			**Q**	**Attempt No.**		
	1	**2**	**3**		**1**	**2**	**3**
1	3			12	6		51
2	6		9	13	1	(-3)	52
3	4		13	14	4		56
4	5		18	15	5	(-1)	
5	3		21	16	5		66
6	5		26	17	5		71
7	4		30	18	3	(-3)	74
8	2	(-2)	32	19	4		78
9	4	(-2)	36	20	6		84
10	5		41	21	3	(-2)	87
11	4		45				
TOTAL	87% (C)						

>80%

GCSE Mathematics
Foundation Tier
Formula Sheet

Area of trapezium $= \dfrac{1}{2}(a + b)h$

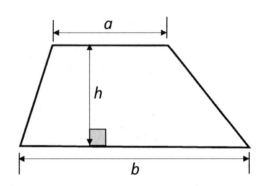

Volume of prism = area of cross-section x length

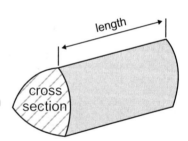

Answer ALL questions.
Write your answers in the spaces provided.

1   **(a)** Write the following numbers in order of size, starting with the smallest.

0.3   30   0.03   0.31   30.1

0.03, 0.3, 0.31, 30, 30.1

(1 mark)

(b) Write the following numbers in order of size, starting with the biggest.

103   25   50   55   101

103, 101, 55, 50, 25

(1 mark)

(c) Write the following numbers in order of size, starting with the smallest.

25%   0.5   1/5   75%   0.1

0.1, 1/5, 25%, 0.5, 75%

(1 mark)

2   Katie is given weekly pocket money for her part-time jobs. Here is how much she earns across six weeks.

£40.60   £32.20   £75.80   £25.00   £15.50   £20.90

(a) Work out the mean.

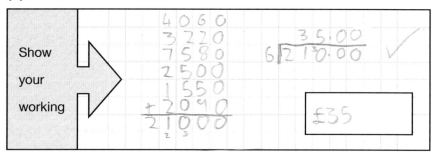

Show your working

4060
3220
7580
2500
1550
+2090
21000

35.00
6)210.00

£35

(2 marks)

21

(b) In week 7, Katie earns £70.30. How much does Katie have altogether?

210 + 70·30 = 280·30

£280·30

(2 marks)

(c) Katie's friend Sarah earns 20% more than Katie's total earnings.

Work out how much Sarah earns.

Show your working

20% = 1/5

```
      56.06
5 2 80.30
```

```
  2 8 0·3 0
+   5 6·0 6
  3 3 6·3 6
```

£336·36

(2 marks)

3 **(a)** Convert 75% to its simplest fraction.

3/4 3/4

(2 marks)

(b) Work out which is the greater value:

60% of 950

Or

3/5 of 1,000

Explain your answer.

3/5 = 60% and 1,000 is larger than 950 so it is 3/5 of 1,000.

(2 marks)

4 Below is a 6-sided polygon.

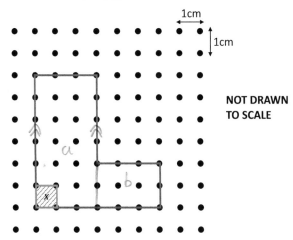

NOT DRAWN
TO SCALE

(a) Write down the mathematical term for a 6-sided shape.

.... hexagon ....

(1 mark)

(b) Write down the mathematical term for the angle marked *x*.

.... right angle ....

(1 mark)

(c) On the diagram above, mark with arrows ⟫ one pair of parallel lines.

(1 mark)

(d) What is the area of the 6-sided polygon?

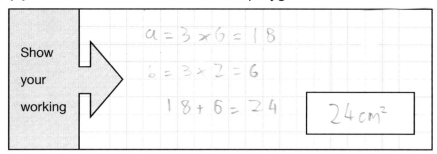

Show

your

working

$a = 3 \times 6 = 18$

$b = 3 \times 2 = 6$

$18 + 6 = 24$

24cm^2

(2 marks)

5 **(a)** What fraction of the shape is shaded?

Write your answer in its simplest form.

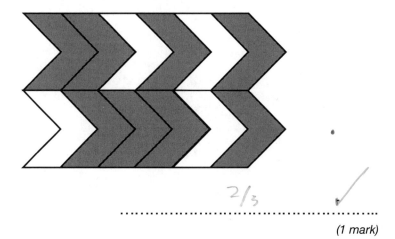

2/3

....

(b) Shade in the other half so that the line becomes a line of symmetry.

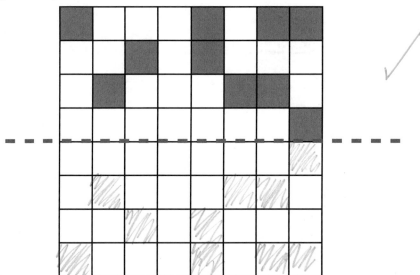

(2 marks)

6 The below tally represents the number of star jumps each person could do in a one minute period. Each person attempted their star jumps three times.

Using the information provided, create a chart or diagram which allows you to compare each person's results.

NAME	TALLY	KEY: ★ = 4 jumps
Rory 1st attempt	★ ★ ★ ★ ★ ★	
2nd attempt	★ ★ ★ ★ ★ ★↓	
3rd attempt	★ ★ ★↓	
Mike 1st attempt	★ ★ ★ ★ ★ ★ ★ ★ ★	
2nd attempt	★ ★ ★ ★ ★ ★	
3rd attempt	★ ★ ★ ★ ★ ★ ★ ★ ★↓	
Phoebe 1st attempt	★ ★ ★ ★↓	
2nd attempt	★ ★ ★ ★ ★ ★	
3rd attempt	★ ★ ★ ★ ★ ★ ★ ★↓	

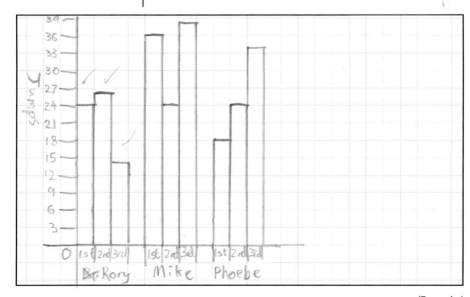

(5 marks)

7 **(a)** Simplify the following fraction.

$$\frac{40}{68} = \frac{20}{34} = \frac{10}{17}$$

Give your answer in its simplest form.

10/17 ✓

(1 mark)

(b) Write $\frac{2}{5}$ as a decimal.

✓

0.4

(1 mark)

*(c)** India says that $\frac{3}{7}$ is bigger than $\frac{2}{3}$.

Is she right? — No ✓

Explain your answer.

India is wrong. I could tell straight away because half of 3 is 1.5, 2 is more than 1.5, and half of 7 is 3.5, 3 is less than 3.5. I could see that 2/3 is more than 1/2 and 3/7 is less, so 2/3 is more.

(2 marks)

8   The diagram shows a circle.

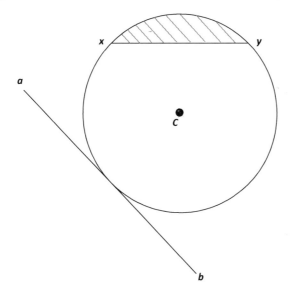

(a) What is the mathematical term for line **xy**?

✓ ...chord...................................

(1 mark)

(b) Work out the length of the **radius**, in millimetres, of the circle.

26·5

...2.6mm...................

(1 mark)

(c) What is the mathematical term for the line **ab**?

✓ ...tangent...................

(1 mark)

(d) Work out the length of the **diameter**, in millimetres, of the circle.

53

...5.2mm...................

(1 mark)

9 Below are three different offers for a 49-inch plasma TV.

Online Store 1

SPECIAL OFFER

Original price =
£268.00

£214.40

Discount =
20% off!

Online Store 2

SPECIAL OFFER

Original price =
£295.00

£221.25

Discount =
$\frac{1}{4}$ off!

Online Store 3

SPECIAL OFFER

Pay £18.50
weekly for 16
weeks

£296

Work out which online store offers the cheapest deal.

You must show **ALL** of your working out.   No 1

```
        5 3 . 6              7
    5 ⟌2 6 8 . 0 0       2 6 8 . 0
                          - 5 3 . 6
        7 3 . 7 5         2 1 4 . 4
    4 ⟌2 9 5 . 0 0
        4   9                   1 8 5 . 0 0
    2 9 5 . 8 0                 × 1 6
    - 7 3 . 7 5                 1 1 1 0
    2 2 1 . 2 5                 1 8 5 0
                               2 9 6 . 0
```

(6 marks)

$\frac{4}{6}$

Did not show answer

10 The bar chart below shows the number of people who applied for a Sales Assistant job.

The job was advertised for one week, and the bars on the chart represent each day of the week up until the closing date.

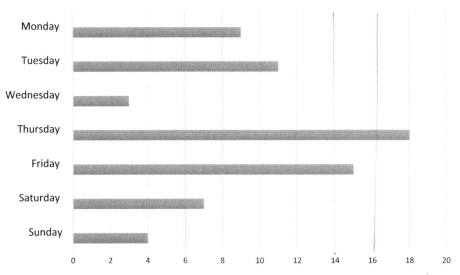

Number of people who applied for a Sales Assistant position

On Wednesday, 3 people applied for the job.

Work out how many people applied for the Sales Assistant position overall.

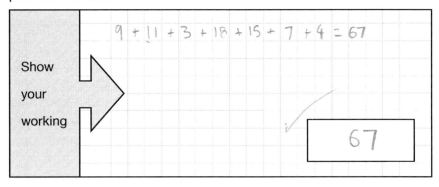

Show your working

$9 + 11 + 3 + 18 + 15 + 7 + 4 = 67$

67

(5 marks)

11 Below is a set of scores for a pop quiz.

The total score for the pop quiz is out of 60, and the marks are recorded for each team that participated.

36   47   52   13   28   29   36   49

(a) Calculate the mean.

36.25

8/290.00   36.25

(1 mark)

(b) Calculate the range.

52 - 13 = 39

(1 mark)

(c) Calculate the median.

36

(1 mark)

(d) Calculate the mode.

36

(1 mark)

12 Here are five cards, each with its own number.

| 5 | 7 | 4 | 1 | 9 |

(a) The above number reads 57,419. Write this number in words.

fifty-seven thousand, four hundred and nineteen

(1 mark)

(b) (i) Write the above number to the nearest **10**.

57,420

(1 mark)

(ii) Write the above number to the nearest **100**.

57,400

(1 mark)

(iii) Write the above number to the nearest **1,000**.

57,000

(1 mark)

(c) Add up all of the numbers on the card.

Calculate the **mean** number. Write your number to the nearest **whole** number. Show your working out.

5 + 7 + 4 + 1 + 9 = 26

26 ÷ 5 = 5.2

5

(2 marks)

13 Below is a triangle.

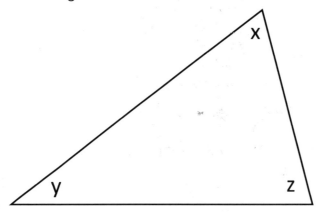

(a) Using a protractor, calculate the angle x.

69° 68°

(1 mark)

(b) Using a protractor, calculate the angle y.

36° 37°

(1 mark)

(c) Using a protractor, calculate the angle z.

75° ✓

(1 mark)

(d) What mathematical term can be used to describe the type of triangle?

scalene

69° acute

(1 mark)

14 Carefully look at the diagram below.

NOT DRAWN TO SCALE

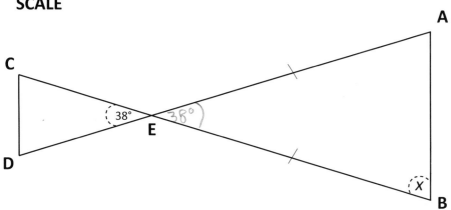

Calculate angle *x*.

Show **ALL** of your working out.

$$
\begin{array}{r}
  \overset{7}{1}\,\overset{}{8}\,0 \\
  -\,3\,8 \\
  \hline
  1\,4\,2
\end{array}
$$

$$
\begin{array}{r}
  7\,1 \\
  2\,\overline{)1\,4\,2}
\end{array}
$$

71°

(4 marks)

15 (a) Work out the value of $6b \div 3c$ when $b = 8$ and $c = 4$.

$(6 \times 8) \div (3 \times 4)$

$48 \div 12 = 4$

Answer = 4 ✓

(2 marks)

(b) Solve $10x = 87$

$x = 8.7$

Answer = 8.7 ✓

(2 marks)

(c) Factorise $6x - 12$

$6(x - 2)$

$\div 6 = x-2$

Answer = $x-2$

(1 mark)

(d) Simplify $9y + 5x - 3y + 4x$

$9y + 5x - 3y + 4x$

$6y + 9x$

Answer = $6y + 9x$ ✓

(1 mark)

16 Below is a grid.

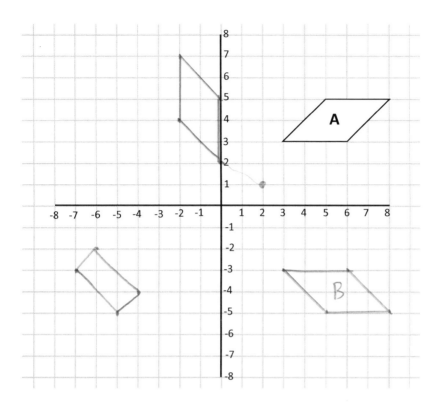

(a) Rotate shape **A** 90° anti-clockwise using the point (2, 1).

(2 marks)

(b) Plot on the grid the following coordinates:

(-7, -3)   (-6, -2)   (-5, -5)   (-4,-4)

(1 mark)

(c) What shape have you just created?

...........rectangle...........

(1 mark)

(d) Reflect shape **A** using the *x* axis as the mirror line. Label your new shape **B**.

(1 mark)

17 Below we have a grid containing letters from A to E.

The total for each **column** and **row** is shown.

A	**A**	**A**	**B**	**D**	24
A	**A**	**B**	**B**	**D**	20
A	**B**	**B**	**C**	**E**	21
A	**B**	**C**	**C**	**E**	22
A	**B**	**C**	**D**	**E**	23
30	18	16	14	32	

Work out the correct values of **A**, **B**, **C**, **D** and **E**.

(i) =   **A** =   6

....

(1 mark)

(ii) =   **B** =   2

....

(1 mark)

(iii) =   **C** =   3

....

(1 mark)

(iv) =   **D** =   4

....

(1 mark)

(v) =   **E** =   8

....

(1 mark)

18 Write the following expressions in their simplest form.

(a) (i) $5x^3 + 4y + 5x - 1y$

$5x^3 + 5x + 3y$ ✓

(1 mark)

(ii) $2y + 3y + 6y - 3y - 3x + 7x$

$+4x$

$8y - 10x$ ✗

(1 mark)

(b) (i) $y + y + 5 + y + 2y - 3$

$+2$

$5y - 2$ ✗

(1 mark)

(ii) $2a + 3a + a - 3y$

$6a - 3y$ ✓

(1 mark)

(c) (i) If $x = -5$ and $y = 2$, work out the value of $4x + 5y$

-10 ✓

(1 mark)

(ii) Factorise completely $4ab - 8a^2$

?

$b - 2a^2$?

(1 mark)

$4a(b - 2a^2)$

19 Look at the shape below.

SCALE = 1cm x 1cm

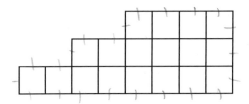

(a) (i) Work out the perimeter.

.............22cm..................

(1 mark)

(ii) Work out the area. Give the correct units.

.............18 cm²..................

(1 mark)

(b) Work out the volume of the shape below, given that each cube is 1x1x1

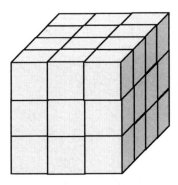

3 x 3 x 4

∴ 9 x 4

∴ = 36

Answer = ...36.......cm²........

(2 marks)

20 Using the common mathematical rule of BIDMAS, complete the following calculations:

(a) (36 ÷ 3) x 4

12

48 ✓

(1 mark)

(b) 5 + 6 x 12

77

(1 mark)

(c) 6 x 2 + 5²

25

37

(1 mark)

(d) 7 x 8 – 4

52

(1 mark)

(e) (46 + 6) – (3³ + 7)

52   34

18

(1 mark)

(f) 12 (24 ÷ 4)

6

72

(1 mark)

21 Sammie has a pack of playing cards. She only uses the suit of hearts.

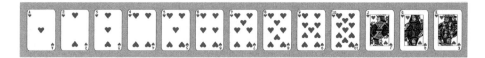

The cards are all faced down, and she plays a game of trying to guess whether the next card is going to be **higher** or **lower**. *For the purpose of this game, the Ace is representing '1'.*

(a) If the first card Sammie picks is the **Queen**, what is the chance of her picking a **higher** card? <u>Please circle your answer.</u>

Certain   Very likely   Likely   Equal   Unlikely   (Very unlikely)   Impossible

(1 mark)

(b) Sammie then picks up a '**4**'. What is the chance of her picking up a '3'? <u>Please circle your answer.</u>

Certain   Very likely   Likely   Equal   Unlikely   (Very unlikely)   Impossible

(1 mark)

(c) Sammie then picks up the **Ace**. What is the chance of her picking a lower number? <u>Please circle your answer.</u>

Certain   Very likely   Likely   Equal   Unlikely   Very unlikely   (Impossible)

(1 mark)

(d) Sammie then picks up a '**2**'. What is the chance of her picking up a higher number? <u>Please circle your answer.</u>

(Certain)   (Very likely)   Likely   Equal   Unlikely   Very unlikely   Impossible

(2 marks)

Ace already chosen

SURNAME		CENTRE NAME				
FIRST NAME/S		CENTRE NUMBER				
CANDIDATE SIGNATURE		CANDIDATE NUMBER				

GCSE Mathematics

SET A
Paper 2 Calculator

Foundation Tier

1 hour and 45 minutes

INSTRUCTIONS TO CANDIDATES

- Use **black** ink.
- **Fill in the boxes** at the top of this page.
- Answer **all** of the questions.
- **Clearly** show your working outs.
- Take the value of π to be 3.142, or use the button π on your calculator.

INFORMATION FOR CANDIDATES

- The **total mark** for this paper is **100**.
- The marks for each question are shown on the **right** side of each page.
- Questions labelled with an asterisk (*) will assess the **quality** of **written communication**.

ADVICE FOR CANDIDATES

- Keep a close eye on the **time**.
- **Do not** spend too long on one question.
- Try to answer **every** question and show your workings out when required.

Q	Attempt No.			Q	Attempt No.		
	1	2	3		1	2	3
1				12			
2				13			
3				14			
4				15			
5				16			
6				17			
7				18			
8				19			
9				20			
10				21			
11							
TOTAL							

For examiner's use

Answer ALL questions.
Write your answers in the spaces provided.

1 **(a)** How many lines of symmetry does the shape below have?

....
(1 mark)

(b) Reflect the shaded shape using the dotted line as a mirror.

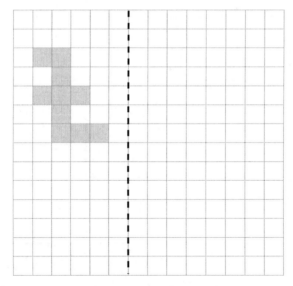

(2 marks)

(c) How many lines of symmetry does the shaded shape in Question 1b have?

....
(1 mark)

2 The shape below contains three triangles and a rectangle.

Work out the area of the total shape. You must show your working out.

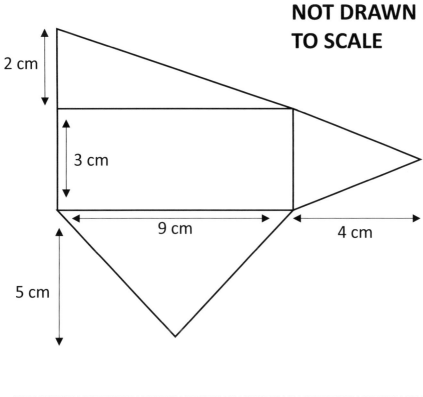

NOT DRAWN TO SCALE

2 cm

3 cm

9 cm

4 cm

5 cm

....

....

....

....

....

Answer = ...

(3 marks)

3 **(a)** Solve $y + 9 = 45$

$y =$...

(1 mark)

(b) Solve $9y = 144$

$y =$...

(1 mark)

(c) Solve $x/4 = 7$

$x =$...

(1 mark)

(d) Solve $7x - 6 = 85$

$x =$...

(1 mark)

4 Match each of the scatter graphs with the correct description.

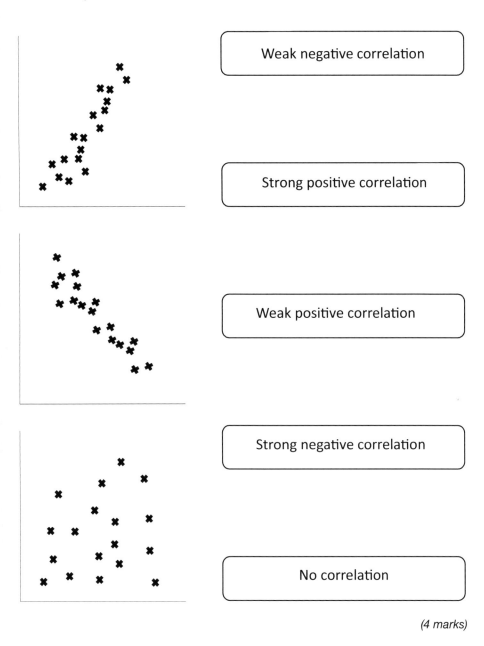

Weak negative correlation

Strong positive correlation

Weak positive correlation

Strong negative correlation

No correlation

(4 marks)

5 Below is a circle.

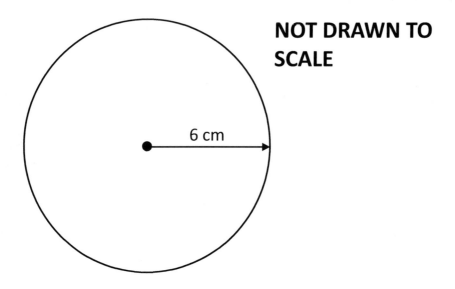

NOT DRAWN TO SCALE

6 cm

As shown, the radius of the circle is 6 cm.

Work out the circumference of the circle. Give the correct answer to 3 significant figures.

....

....

....

....

....

Answer = ...

(3 marks)

6 **(a)** (i) Use your calculator to work out $\dfrac{7.4 \times 9.2}{21.8-9}$

You should write down all of the numbers that are displayed on your calculator. Your answer should be written as a decimal.

Answer = ...

(2 marks)

(ii) Write your answer from part (6ai), to 2 decimal places.

Answer = ...

(1 mark)

(b) Use your calculator to work out the value of the calculation below.

$\sqrt[3]{216}$

Answer = ...

(2 marks)

7 Below is a 1 cm by 1cm grid.

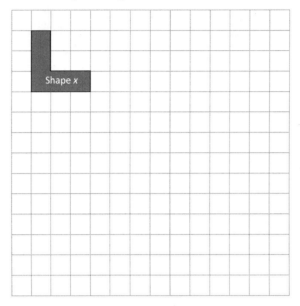

(a) Draw on the grid an enlargement of shape *x*, which has a scale factor of 3.

(2 marks)

*(b) Describe the transformation that maps shape ***A*** onto shape ***B***.

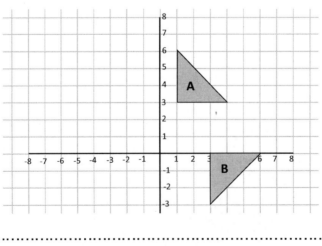

....

....

....

(2 marks)

8 Below is a right angled triangle.

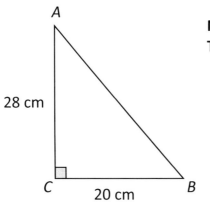

NOT DRAWN
TO SCALE

28 cm

20 cm

A

C

B

(a) Work out the length of side *AB*. Write your answer to the nearest whole number. You must show **ALL** of your working out.

....

....

....

Answer = ...

(3 marks)

(b) Work out the angle labelled **X**.

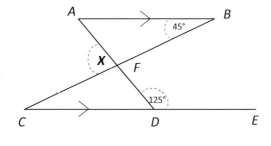

AB and *CE* are parallel lines
Angle *ABC* = 45°
Angle *FDE* = 125°

....

....

....

Answer = ...

(3 marks)

9 Sammie puts 8 large marbles and 6 small marbles in a bag.

Without looking, Sammie puts her hand in the bag and pulls out one of the marbles.

(a) What are the odds of Sammie picking a small marble? Write your answer as a fraction and in its simplest form.

Answer = ...

(2 marks)

(b) If the probability remains the same, but 28 more balls are added, what is the fraction of large marbles? Write your answer in its simplest form.

Answer = ...

(2 marks)

10 The below pie chart shows information about the number of people who are unemployed between the ages of 18 and 40.

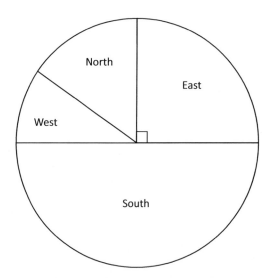

(a) What is the percentage of people who are unemployed and living in the East?

Answer = ...

(1 mark)

*(b) Write one comparison between unemployment levels in the South and the East.

....

....

....

(2 marks)

(c) If there are 3,600 unemployed people living in the East, how many unemployed people are there altogether?

....

....

....

(2 marks)

11 Here are four match sticks.

Pattern 1

The pattern continues as follows:

Pattern 1   Pattern 2   Pattern 3

(a) How many match sticks would be in pattern 9?

....

....

....

Answer = ...

(2 marks)

(b) If n represents the number of match sticks, and p represents the pattern number, write the rule to work out the next pattern in the sequence.

....

....

....

Answer = ...

(2 marks)

(c) Using your answer from (part b), work out how many match sticks would be needed for the 85th pattern.

....

....

....

Answer = ...

(2 marks)

12 Jason is building a fence around his garden.

The diagram below shows the shape of Jason's garden with some of the measurements he is going to need.

NOT DRAWN TO SCALE

(a) Write down the measurements of **X** and **Y**.

X = ...

Y = ...

(2 marks)

(b) Write down the perimeter of Jason's garden.

....

....

....

Answer = ...

(2 marks)

(c) Jason is working out how much fencing he needs. Per meter, it is going to cost £1.05.

Use your calculator to work out the total cost of building the fence.

....

....

....

Answer = ...

(2 marks)

13 Below is a distance chart between five destinations.

The chart gives the driving distances, in kilometres.

				Destination A
			Destination B	124
		Destination C	76	300
	Destination D	480	203	217
Destination E	375	418	390	264

Tamsyn will be driving at an average speed of 60 mph.

If 5 miles is approximately 8 km, how long will it take Tamsyn to drive from Destination C to Destination D?

You must show **ALL** of your working out.

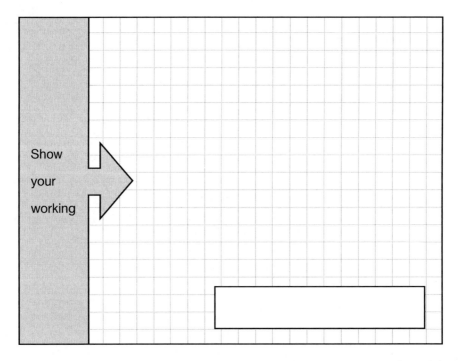

Show

your

working

(5 marks)

14 A school has organised a school trip to London to see a show.

In total there are 45 children and 9 adults attending.

(a) Work out the ratio of children to adults attending the trip. Give your answer in its simplest form.

Answer = ...

(1 mark)

(b) The price for children to attend this trip is £36.70. The price for adults is £48.10. Work out the total price of the trip.

....

....

....

Answer = ...

(2 marks)

(c) The total price is deducted by 20% for booking in advance. Work out the new price of the overall school trip.

....

....

....

Answer = ...

(2 marks)

15 Luke records the type of dogs his classmates have.

Types of dogs	Tally	Frequency
Labrador	ⅢⅠ |||	
Golden Retriever		3
Chihuahua		3
Pug	||	
Yorkshire Terrier	||||	
Other		9

(a) Complete the tally graph above.

(1 mark)

(b) What fraction of the total number of dogs are Yorkshire Terriers? Write your fraction in its simplest form.

Answer = ...

(1 mark)

(c) If the number of people recorded were 3 times as many as the records shown above, and tripled the frequencies, how many people have a Labrador?

....

....

....

Answer = ...

(2 marks)

16 The diagram below shows the layout of an animal sanctuary.

The animal sanctuary contains 6 separate enclosures for different animals.

The animal sanctuary is a rectangle with the following dimensions:

48 metres by 24 metres

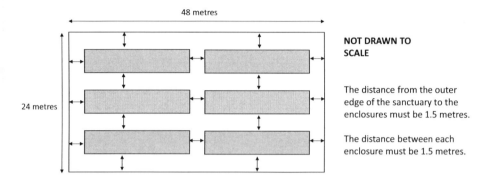

NOT DRAWN TO SCALE

The distance from the outer edge of the sanctuary to the enclosures must be 1.5 metres.

The distance between each enclosure must be 1.5 metres.

Each enclosure is the exact same size. Using the information provided in the diagram above, work out the length and height of the enclosures.

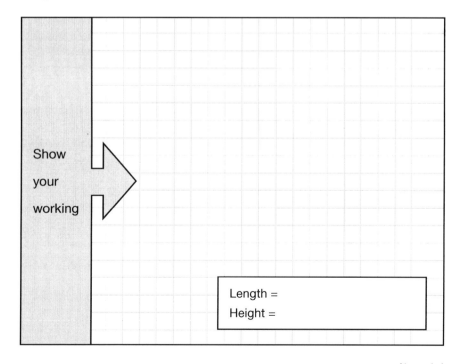

Show your working

Length =

Height =

(4 marks)

17 Write these numbers in order of size, starting with the smallest.

(a) 56%   0.5   2/5

Answer = …………………………………………..

(1 mark)

Write these numbers in order of size, starting with the largest.

(b) 60% of 400   1/3 of 360   Half of 796

Answer = …………………………………………..

(1 mark)

Circle the fraction that is greater than 1/2 but less than 3/4

(c) 2/5   1/3   5/8   4/8

(1 mark)

(d) Write the number twenty seven thousand three hundred and thirteen in figures.

Answer = …………………………………………..

(1 mark)

(e) Write the number 103,501 in words.

…………………………………………………………………..

…………………………………………………………………..

(1 mark)

(f) Write the number 43.147 to 2 decimal places.

Answer = …………………………………………..

(1 mark)

18 Look at the sequence below:

1   9   17   25   33   ...   ...

(a) (i) What are the next **two** terms in the sequence?

Answer = ...
(1 mark)

(ii) Using the sequence above, explain in words the rule needed to progress in the sequence.

Answer = ...
(1 mark)

(b) (i) A sequence uses the following rule:

n^{th} term = $3(n + 1)$

Work out the first six terms in this sequence, using the rule provided. 'N' represents the term number in the sequence. Fill in the table below with your answers.

1st term	2nd term	3rd term	4th term	5th term	6th term

(2 marks)

*(ii) Explain why **46** is not in the above sequence.

....

....

....

(2 marks)

19 (a) Two of the numbers move from Box A to Box B. The total of the numbers in Box B is now four times the total of the numbers in Box A. Which two numbers move?

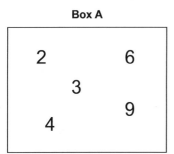

Box A

Box B

Answer = ...

(2 marks)

(b) Below is a spinner which has 10 equal sections.

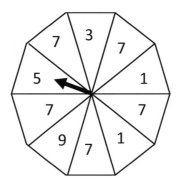

(i) What are the odds of the arrow landing on the number **9**?

Impossible	Unlikely	Likely	Certain

(1 mark)

(ii) What are the odds of the arrow landing on an **even** number?

Impossible	Unlikely	Likely	Certain

(1 mark)

(iii) What are the odds of the arrow landing on the number **1**?

Impossible	Unlikely	Likely	Certain

(1 mark)

20 Look at the grid of shapes below and answer the following questions.

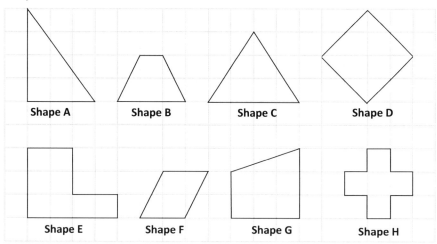

Shape A Shape B Shape C Shape D

Shape E Shape F Shape G Shape H

(a) Which shape has 3 orders of rotation?

Answer = ...

(1 mark)

(b) Which shapes have more than one parallel line?

Answer = ...

(1 mark)

(c) Which shapes contain a right angle?

Answer = ...

(1 mark)

(d) What is the area of shape D?

Answer = ...

(1 mark)

(e) What is the correct name of shape F?

Answer = ...

(1 mark)

21 (a) Factorise:

12 + 20x

Answer = ...

(1 mark)

(b) Factorise:

$x^2 - 81$

Answer = ...

(1 mark)

(c) Solve:

$6(x - 3) = x + 7$

Answer = ...

(1 mark)

(d) Simplify:

$a^2 + a^2$

Answer = ...

(1 mark)

(e) Factorise completely:

$20a^2 - 10a$

Answer = ...

(2 marks)

GCSE

Mathematics

SET A

Calculator and Non-Calculator Paper
Foundation Tier

ANSWER BOOKLET

1. (a) 0.03, 0.3, 0.31, 30, 30.1

Pay attention to where the decimal point is. It can be confusing because some of the numbers only have 2 numbers, whereas some have 3. You can always add a '0' to the end of the numbers, so that all of the decimals contain the same amount of numbers:

  0.03   0.30   0.31   30.0   30.1

1 mark

1. (b) 103,   101,   55,   50,   25

Be sure to pay attention to what the question is asking you. This is a simple question, but it is asking you to write the numbers starting with the BIGGEST.

1 mark

Award no marks if answer is written from smallest to biggest.

1. (c) 0.1,   1/5,   25%,   0.5,   75%

Convert the numbers all into percentages to work out the order of size.

  0.1 = 10%
  1/5 = 20%
  25%
  0.5 = 50%
  75%

1 mark

2. (a) £35.00

To work out the mean:

$$
\begin{array}{r}
40.60 \\
32.20 \\
75.80 \\
25.00 \\
15.50 \\
+ \quad 20.90 \\
\hline
210.00
\end{array}
$$

210 ÷ 6 = 35

2 marks

(1 mark for adding up the total amount).

(1 mark for correctly dividing by how many numbers there are).

2. (b) £280.30

In week 7, Katie earns £70.30. In total, she has:

$$
\begin{array}{r}
210.00 \\
+ \quad 70.30 \\
\hline
280.30
\end{array}
$$

2 marks

(1 mark for having the correct total across the first 6 weeks).

(1 mark for correctly adding both amounts).

2. (c) £336.36

Katie's earnings £280.30

Sarah earns 20% more.

10% of 280.30 = 28.03

20% = 28.03 + 28.03 = 56.06

So Sarah earns 280.30 + 56.06 = 336.36

2 marks

(1 mark for working out 20% of Katie's earnings)

(1 mark for adding Katie's earnings with the 20%).

3. (a) ¾

75% as a fraction = 75 over 100 = 75/100

Both of these numbers can be divided by 25 to simplify it to: 3/4.

2 marks

(1 mark for converting it to a fraction).

(1 mark for the answer being written in its simplest form).

3. (b) 3/5 of 1,000 is the greater value.

60% of 950 = 950 ÷ 100 = 9.5

9.5 x 60 = 570.

3/5 of 1000 = 1000 ÷ 5 = 200

200 x 3 = 600.

Therefore 3/5 of 1000 is the greater value.

2 marks

(1 mark for working out each part of the calculation).

4. (a) hexagon

A six-sided shape is a hexagon.

1 mark

4. (b) right angle

An angle at 90° is a right angle.

1 mark

4. (c) You could have marked the following parallel lines:

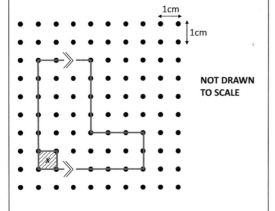

NOT DRAWN
TO SCALE

1 mark

(You could have also marked the two vertical sides. Parallel lines are lines that are the same distance apart and are not touching).

4. (d) 24 cm²

The 6 sided shape is drawn on a 1x1 grid which means each square represents 1cm. The shape covers 24 squares, so this is the area.

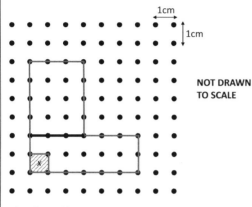

4 x 3 = 12

2 x 6 = 12

12 + 12 = 24 cm²

2 marks

(1 mark for the correct answer).

(1 mark for showing how you calculated the correct answer).

5. (a) 2/3

8 of the arrows are shaded. There are 12 arrows in total. Therefore the fraction of shaded arrows is 8/12.

Both numbers can be divided by 4, to simplify it to: 2/3.

1 mark

(Award no marks if the fraction has not been simplified).

5. (b) Your answer should look like this:

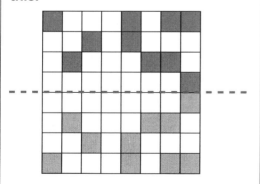

2 marks

(Award 2 marks for all correct squares shaded in. Only award 1 mark if one of the squares has been shaded in incorrectly. Award 0 marks if more than 1 square has been shaded in incorrectly).

6. You need to draw a chart to compare the results. A bar chart or line graph would be a great way to compare each of their results.

Your chart could look something like this:

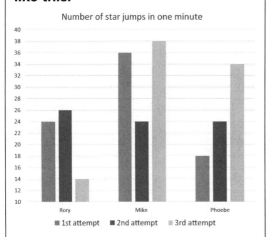

Number of star jumps in one minute

Rory   Mike   Phoebe

■ 1st attempt   ■ 2nd attempt   ▨ 3rd attempt

5 marks

(Award the five marks for the correct data inserted into a graph that compares all three people's results, with each of their attempts).

7. (a) 10/17

40/68 = both numbers can be divided by 4.

1 mark

7. (b) 0.4

2/5 as a decimal:

$2 \div 5 = 0.4$

You could also work it out like so:

$100 \div 5 = 20 \times 2 = 40\%$

$40 \div 100 = 0.4$

1 mark

7. (c) India is not right. 3/7 is not bigger than 2/3.

You need to change the denominator so that they are both the same.

The denominator '7' and '3' can be changed to the same denominator, which in this case is '21' (both numbers can go into 21).

    3/7 = 9/21

    2/3= 14/21

2 marks

(1 mark for correct answer).

(1 mark for quality of written communication demonstrated in workings out).

8. (a) chord

1 mark

8. (b) 26.5 mm

1 mark

8. (c) 53 mm

1 mark

8. (d) 96 mm

1 mark

9. Online Store 1 offers the cheapest deal

Online Store 1 = 20% off £268.00

    10% = 26.80

    20% = 26.80 + 26.80 = 53.60

    268.00 – 53.60 = £214.40

Online Store 2 = ¼ off £295

    295 ÷ 4 = 73.75

    295 – 73.75 = £221.25

Online Store 3 = £18.50 for 16 weeks

    18.50 x 16 = £296

Therefore Online Store 1 offers the best deal.

6 marks

(Award 2 marks for correct answer).

(Award 1 mark for attempt of showing working out)

(Award 1 mark for correct working out to online store 1)

(Award 1 mark for correct working out to online store 2)

(Award 1 mark for correct working out to online store 3)

10. 67 people applied for the job	5 marks
Each line on the graph represents '2'.	(Award 2 marks for correct answer)
Monday = 9	(Award 3 marks for adding up correctly the bars in the chart. Award 2 marks for no more than one error. Award 1 mark for no more than two errors).

10. 67 people applied for the job

Each line on the graph represents '2'.

    Monday = 9

    Tuesday = 11

    Wednesday = 3

    Thursday = 18

    Friday = 15

    Saturday = 7

    Sunday = 4

    9 + 11 + 3 + 18 + 15 + 7 + 4 = 67

5 marks

(Award 2 marks for correct answer)

(Award 3 marks for adding up correctly the bars in the chart. Award 2 marks for no more than one error. Award 1 mark for no more than two errors).

11. (a) 36.25

To work out the mean:

    36 + 47 + 52 + 13 + 28 + 29 + 36 + 49 = 290

    290 ÷ 8 = 36.25

1 mark

11. (b) 39

To calculate the range:

Biggest number (52) – smallest number (13) = 39.

1 mark

11. (c) 36

To calculate the median, you need to arrange the numbers from smallest to biggest, and then work out which number is in the middle.

    13 28 29 36 36 47 49 52

1 mark

11. (d) 36

To calculate the mode, you need to see which number appears the most.

    '36' appears twice, no other number appears more times, and therefore this is the mode.

1 mark

12. (a) fifty seven thousand four hundred and nineteen	1 mark
The best way to write out the number is to read it out loud.	
12. (b) (i) 57,420	1 mark
To the nearest 10, the number 57,419 will be rounded up to 57,420.	
The '9' in the units column determines what happens to the number in the tens column.	
12. (b) (ii) 57,400	1 mark
To the nearest 100, the number 57,419 will be rounded down to 57,400.	
The number '1' in the tens column determines what happens to the number in the hundreds column.	
12. (b) (iii) 57,000	1 mark
To the nearest 1,000, the number 57,419 will be rounded down to 57,000.	
The number '4' in the hundreds column determines what happens to the number in the thousands column.	
12. (c) 5 $5 + 7 + 4 + 1 + 9 = 26$ $26 \div 5 = 5.2$ *To the nearest whole number = 5*	2 marks (1 mark for correct answer). (1 mark for showing workings out).
13. (a) 68°	1 mark
13. (b) 37°	1 mark
13. (c) 75°	1 mark

13. (d) scalene

A scalene triangle has all different side lengths and different size angles.

1 mark

14. Angle x is 71°

The angle opposite the angle labelled 38°, is also 38°. Opposite angles are the same size.

180 − 38 = 142

Both the sides of the triangle are of the same size (it is an isosceles triangle). Therefore the angles will be the same size.

142 ÷ 2 = 71°

4 marks

(2 marks for correct answer).

(2 marks for showing workings out).

15. (a) 4

If b = 8 and c = 4

6 x 8 = 48

3 x 4 = 12

48 ÷ 12 = 4

2 marks

(Award 1 mark for correct answer).

(Award 1 mark for showing correct calculations).

15. (b) 8.7

10x = 87

87 ÷ 10 = 8.7

10 x 8.7 = 87

2 marks

(Award 1 mark for correct answer).

(Award 1 mark for showing correct calculations).

15. (c)   6(x − 2)

The highest common factor is 6.

So:

6x − 12

6(x − 2)

1 mark

15. (d)   6y + 9x

(9y) (+ 5x) (– 3y) (+ 4x)

(9y) (– 3y) = 6y

(+ 5x) (+ 4x) = + 9x

6y + 9x

1 mark

16. (a) Your answer should look like this:

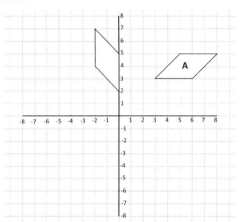

2 marks

(Award 1 mark for rotating in the correct direction).

(Award 1 mark for drawing the shape in its correct position).

16. (b) Your answer should look like this:

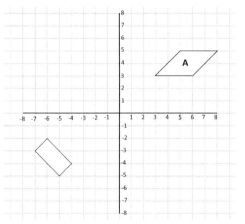

1 mark

16. (c) Rectangle

The shape you have just created is a rectangle.

1 mark

16. (d) Your answer should look like this:

1 mark

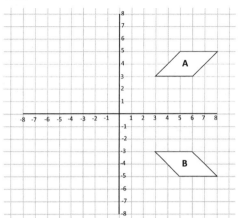

17. (i) A = 6

1 mark

The first column has a total of 30. The only letter in that column is A, so A is:

    30 ÷ 5 (rows) = 6

17. (ii) B = 2

1 mark

    18 – 12 = 6

    6 ÷ 3 = 2

17. (iii) C = 3

1 mark

    6 + 2 + 2 = 10

    16 – 10 = 6

    6 ÷ 2 = 3

17. (iv) D = 4

1 mark

    2 + 2 + 3 + 3 = 10

    14 – 10 = 4

17. (v) E = 8

1 mark

    4 + 4 = 8

    32 – 8 = 24

    24 ÷ 3 = 8

18. (a) (i) 5x³ + 3y + 5x   1 mark

    ($5x^3$) (+4y) (+5x) (-1y)

    ($5x^3$)

    (+4y) (-1y) = +3y

    (+5x)

    $5x^3$ + 3y + 5x

18. (a) (ii) 8y + 4x   1 mark

    2y + 3y + 6y - 3y = 8y

    -3x + 7x = + 4x

18. (b) (i) 5y + 2   1 mark

    y + y + y + 2y = 5y

    +5 – 3 = +2

    5y + 2

18. (b) (ii) 6a – 3y   1 mark

    2a + 3a + a = 6a

    6a – 3y

18. (c) (i) -10   1 mark

    4 x -5 = -20

    5 x 2 = 10

    -20 + 10 = -10

18. (c) (ii) 4a(b – 2a)   1 mark

You need to work out the largest possible factor to use outside of the brackets.

Both 4 and 8 have the factor of 4. Both parts of the expression contain an 'a', so this can also be written outside of the brackets.

    4a (b – 2a)

19. (a) (i) 22   1 mark

You need to add up all of the sides of the outside of the shape. Remember the scale of the shape is 1cm by 1cm.

19. (a) (ii) 18 cm²   1 mark

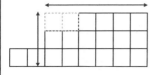 Width = 6 cm
Height = 3 cm
Area = 6 x 3 = 18 cm²

19. (b) 36 cm³   2 marks

     3 x 3 x 4 = 36 cm³

20. (a) 48   1 mark

     36 ÷ 3 = 12

     12 x 4 = 48

20. (b) 77   1 mark

     6 x 12 = 72

     5 + 72 = 77

20. (c) 37   1 mark

     5 x 5 = 25

     6 x 2 = 12

     12 + 25 = 37

20. (d) 52   1 mark

     7 x 8 = 56

     56 – 4 = 52

20. (e) 18   1 mark

     46 + 6 = 52

     3 x 3 x 3 = 27 + 7 = 34

     52 – 34 = 18

20. (f) 72

$24 \div 4 = 6$

$12 \times 6 = 72$

1 mark

21. (a) Very unlikely

If Sammie picks a Queen, the chances of picking a higher card is very unlikely. The only higher card is the King, so the odds of picking that card are very slim.

1 mark

21. (b) Very unlikely

The chances of Sammie picking up a 3 has the probability of 1 in 10. (Remember the Queen has already been taken, so you would not include this in the probability scale).

1 mark

21. (c) Impossible

If Sammie picks up the Ace, there is no chance of picking up a lower card, because the Ace is the lowest card.

You would need to have read the question carefully to know that the Ace in this card game is low and not high.

1 mark

21. (d) Certain

The chances of picking up a higher card is certain. Sammie has already picked up the Ace, meaning that no lower cards can be picked up. Therefore the card she picks up next is guaranteed to be higher.

2 marks

SET A – PAPER 2
(Calculator)

1. (a) The shape contains 1 line of symmetry	1 mark
Pay attention to where the lines are going through the star.	
1. (b) Your answer should look like this: 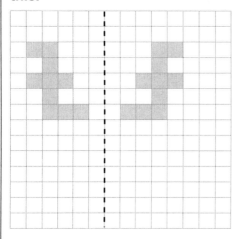	2 marks (2 marks for all squares correctly shaded).
1. (c) 0	1 mark
The shaded shape in Question 1b does not contain any lines of symmetry.	

2. 64.5 cm²
 	
    3 x 9 = 27
    9 x 5 = 45 ÷ 2 = 22.5
    9 x 2 = 18 ÷ 2 = 9
    3 x 4 = 12 ÷ 2 = 6
    27 + 22.5 + 9 + 6 = 64.5 cm²
	3 marks
	
	(1 mark for correct answer).
	
	(2 marks for showing all working out. Award 1 mark for no more than one error in workings out).

3. (a) y = 36

45 − 9 = 36

36 + 9 = 45

1 mark

3. (b) y = 16

144 ÷ 9 = 16

9 x 16 = 144

1 mark

3. (c) x = 28

4 x 7 = 28

28 ÷ 4 = 7

1 mark

3. (d) x = 13

85 + 6 = 91

91 ÷ 7 = 13

7 x 13 = 91 − 6 = 85

1 mark

4. The first chart should be linked up to 'Strong positive correlation'.

The second chart should be liked up to 'Strong negative correlation'.

The third chart should be linked up to 'No correlation'.

4 marks

(Award 4 marks for all 3 correct answers. Award 3 marks for 2 correct answers. Award 2 marks for 1 correct answer).

5. 37.7

To work out the circumference of the circle:

> *Radius = 6 cm*

> *Diameter = 12 cm*

You will need your calculator. Push the 'Pi' symbol and multiply it by 12 (the diameter):

> *37.69911…*

To three significant figures = 37.7

3 marks

(Award 1 mark for writing answer as three significant figures).

(Award 1 mark for correct answer despite not being rounded to the correct figures).

(Award 1 mark for showing working out).

6. (a) (i) 5.31875

$7.4 \times 9.2 = 68.08$

$21.8 - 9 = 12.8$

$68.08 \div 12.8 = 5.31875$

2 marks

(Award 1 mark for correct answer).

(Award 1 mark for showing workings out).

6. (a) (ii) 5.32

1 mark

Using your answer to part (6ai), you need to round the number to 2 decimal places.

This would become 5.32 = the '8' determines whether to round up or round down, and because this number is higher than 5, we round up.

6. (b) 6

You would need to use your calculator in order to work out this question.

Type in the number and push the button: $\sqrt[3]{x}$

2 marks

(Award 2 marks for correct answer, and using the correct button on the calculator).

7. (a) Your answer should look like this:

2 marks

(Award 1 mark for enlarging each side by the factor of 3; 3 multiplied the number of each side).

(Award 1 mark for shading in the shape).

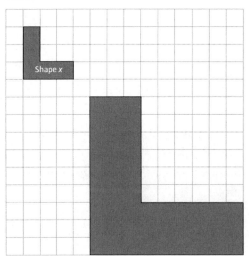

Shape x

7. (b) Rotation

To get from shape A to shape B, the shape has been rotated 90° clockwise using the point (0,0).

2 marks

(1 mark for correct transformation).

(1 mark for quality of written communication).

8. (a) 34 cm

ACB = right angle

AC = 28 cm

BC = 20 cm

$$AB = 28^2 + 20^2$$
$$= 784 + 400 = 1184$$
$$= \sqrt{1184} = 34.4093...$$

To the nearest whole number = 34 cm.

3 marks

(Award 1 mark for correct answer).

(Award 1 mark for finding the square numbers of 28 and 20).

(Award 1 mark for finding the square root of 1184).

8. (b) x = 100°

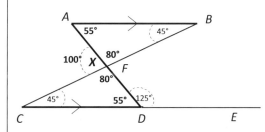

Angle BCD = 45°

180 − 125 = 55°

Angle BAD = 55°

180 − 45 − 55 = 80°

360 − 80 − 80 = 200

200 ÷ 2 = 100, so angle x and f are 100°

3 marks

(Award 1 mark for correct answer).

(Award 1 mark working out the alternate angles on parallel lines).

(Award 1 mark for adding up the angles in a triangle).

9. (a) 3/7

There are 6 small marbles in the bag. There are 14 marbles altogether. So the odds of Sammie picking a small marble is 6/14 or 3/7.

2 marks

(1 mark for correct fraction).

(1 mark for the fraction being in its simplest form).

9. (b) 4/7

If the probability remains the same, and 28 more marbles are added, that means there are now 24 large marbles, and 18 small marbles.

The fraction of large marbles out of the overall total is 24/42 or 4/7.

2 marks

(1 mark for correct fraction).

(1 mark for the fraction being in its simplest form).

10. (a) 25%

25% of people are unemployed and are living in the East.

1 mark

10. (b) The South has double the amount of unemployed people compared to the people living in the East.

2 marks

(1 mark for correct comparison).

(1 mark for quality of written communication).

10. (c) 14,400

3,600 x 4 = 14,400

2 marks

11. (a) 28

In each pattern, the number of match sticks is increasing by 3 each time.

To work out the pattern, you will need to multiply the pattern number by 3 and then add 1.

To work out pattern number 9:

9 x 3 = 27 + 1 = 28

2 marks

(1 mark for correct answer).

(1 mark for showing workings out).

11. (b) number of match sticks (n) = pattern number (p) x 3 + 1

To progress in this sequence, you need to multiply the pattern number by 3, and then add 1.

2 marks

(1 mark for correct answer).

(1 mark for showing workings out).

11. (c) 256

Number of match sticks = 85 (pattern number) x 3 = 255 + 1 = 256

2 marks

(1 mark for correct answer).

(1 mark for showing workings out).

12. (a) x = 5 m
y = 4 m

You need to use the side lengths already given to work out the side lengths missing.

For example, to work out side x, you know that this is parallel to the side to the left, and is the same height, therefore this must be the same as 5 m.

To work out side y, you know that the total width is 14 m (2 + 4 + 8). So to work out side y, 14 – 6 – 4 = 4 m.

2 marks

(1 mark for correct side length for y).

(1 mark for correct side length for x).

12. (b) 48 m

To work out the perimeter of Jason's garden:

> *5 + 6 + 2 + 4 + 2 + 4 + 5 + 8 + 3 + 4 + 3 + 2 = 48 m*

2 marks

(1 mark for correct answer).

(1 mark for showing working outs).

12. (c) £50.40

> *48 metres x £1.05 = £50.40*

2 marks

(1 mark for correct answer).

(1 mark for showing working outs).

13. 5 hours

Destination C to destination D = 480 kilometres

If 5 miles is approximately 8 km:

> *480 ÷ 8 x 5 = 300 (this converts the kilometres into miles).*

To work out the time, you need to divide the distance by the speed:

$$\frac{300}{60} = 5$$

Therefore it would take Tamsyn 5 hours.

5 marks

(Award 1 mark for correct answer).

(Award 2 marks for correctly converting kilometres into miles).

(Award 2 marks for correctly dividing the distance by speed).

14. (a) 5 : 1

The ratio of children to adults is 45 : 9.

Both 45 and 9 are divisible by 9.

In its simplest form the ratio is 5 : 1. (There are 5 students to every 1 adult).

1 mark

14. (b) £2084.40

36.70 x 45 = 1651.50

48.10 x 9 = 432.90

1651.50 + 432.90 = £2084.40

2 marks

(1 mark for correct answer).

(1 mark for showing all working out).

14. (c) £1667.52

Total cost = 2084.40

10% of this = 208.44

So 20% = 208.44 x 2 = 416.88

20% off = 2084.40 − 416.88 = £1667.52

2 marks

(1 mark for correct answer).

(1 mark for showing all working out).

15. (a) Your answer should look like this:

1 mark

Types of dogs	Tally	Frequency
Labrador	𝗜𝗜𝗜𝗜𝗜 𝗜𝗜𝗜	8
Golden Retriever	𝗜𝗜𝗜	3
Chihuahua	𝗜𝗜𝗜	3
Pug	𝗜𝗜	2
Yorkshire Terrier	𝗜𝗜𝗜𝗜	4
Other	𝗜𝗜𝗜𝗜𝗜 𝗜𝗜𝗜𝗜	9

15. (b) 4/29

The total number of dogs is 29. The number of Yorkshire Terriers is 4. So this is 4/29.

1 mark

15. (c) 24

If the number of people recorded was three times as many and the tally and frequency chart tripled the results, the number of people who have a Labrador is 3 times as many:
8 x 3 = 24.

2 mark

(Award 1 mark for correct answer).

(Award 1 mark for having the correct total overall for the results).

16. Length of each enclosure = 21.75 metres

Height of each enclosure = 6 metres

To work out the length = total 48 metres

48 – 1.5 – 1.5 – 1.5 = 43.5

43.5 ÷ 2 = 21.75 metres

To work out the height = total 24 metres

24 – 1.5 – 1.5 – 1.5 – 1.5 = 18

18 ÷ 3 = 6 metres

4 marks

(2 marks for both correct answers).

(1 mark for working out the height. 1 mark for working out the length).

17. (a) 2/5,　0.5,　56%

You need to convert these numbers so that they are either all percentages, decimals or fractions.

Let's change them all into percentages:

    56%

    0.5 = 50%

    2/5 = 40%

So smallest to largest = 2/5, 0.5, 56%

1 mark

**17. (b) Half of 796,   60% of 400,
1/3 of 360**

60% of 400

   400 ÷ 100 x 60 = 240

1/3 of 360

   360 ÷ 3 = 120

Half of 796

   796 ÷ 2 = 398

*So largest to smallest is = half of 796,
60% of 400, 1/3 of 360*

1 mark

17. (c) 5/8

*You can rule out 4/8 because that is
equivalent to 1/2.*

*2/5 and 1/3 are smaller than 1/2 so
it cannot be these. Therefore the
correct answer is 5/8.*

1 mark

17. (d) 27,313

*Read out the sentence and write the
numbers as you go.*

1 mark

**17. (e) One hundred and three
thousand five hundred and one.**

*Read out the numbers and write it as
you go.*

1 mark

17. (f) 43.15

1 mark

18. (a) (i) 41,   49

*The number sequence is adding 8 to
the previous number.*

1 mark

**18. (a) (ii) You need to add 8 to the
previous number.**

1 mark

18. (b) (i) Your answer should look like this:

1st term	2nd term	3rd term	4th term	5th term	6th term
6	9	12	15	18	21

2 marks

(Award 2 marks for all 6 correct numbers. Award 1 mark for no more than two errors).

18. (b) (ii) 46 is not in the above sequence because 48 is in the sequence and therefore 46 cannot be.

To reach 48, this would be the 15th pattern:

$$15 + 1 = 16 \times 3 = 48.$$

Even if you were to try the 14th pattern to reach 46 this would not work:

$$14 + 1 = 15 \times 3 = 45$$

2 marks

(1 mark for explaining how it is not in the sequence).

(1 mark for quality of written communication demonstrated by examples).

19. (a) 4 and 9

If you move 9 and 4 from Box A that leaves the total of:

$$6 + 3 + 2 = 11$$

If you add the 9 and 4 to Box B, you will get a total of:

$$9 + 4 + 10 + 1 + 7 + 5 + 8 = 44$$

Therefore the total of box B is now four times bigger than box A.

2 marks

(Award 1 mark for moving each correct answer).

19. (b) (i) Unlikely

There is one chance out of 10 of the arrow landing on the number 9.

1 mark

19. (b) (ii) Impossible

There are no even numbers on the spinner.

1 mark

19. (b) (iii) Unlikely

There are 2 chances out of 10 to land on the number 1.

1 mark

20. (a) Shape C

The equilateral triangle has 3 orders of rotation.

1 mark

20. (b) Shape D, Shape E, Shape F, Shape H

Parallel sides are sides that are exactly the same width apart and are not touching.

1 mark

20. (c) Shape A, Shape D, Shape E, Shape G, Shape H

A right angle is an angle of 90°.

1 mark

20. (d) 8 cm²

There are 4 whole squares.

There are 8 ½ squares.

8 ½ squares = 4

4 + 4 = 8

1 mark

20. (e) Parallelogram

A parallelogram is a quadrilateral shape with opposite sides that are parallel.

1 mark

21. (a)   4 (3 + 5x)

1 mark

21. (b)   (x + 9) (x – 9)

1 mark

21. (c) x = 5

(5 – 3 = 2)

2 x 6 = 12

5 + 8 = 12

1 mark

21. (d) 2a²

a + a = 2a

Both of these are being squared, so 2a squared = 2a².

1 mark

21. (e) 10a (2a − 1)

Highest common factor = 10

10a (2a − 1)

= 20a² - 10a

2 marks

SURNAME		CENTRE NAME				
FIRST NAME/S		CENTRE NUMBER				
CANDIDATE SIGNATURE		CANDIDATE NUMBER				

GCSE Mathematics

SET B
Paper 1 Non-Calculator

Foundation Tier

1 hour and 45 minutes

INSTRUCTIONS TO CANDIDATES

- Use **black** ink.
- **Fill in the boxes** at the top of this page.
- Answer **all** of the questions.
- **Clearly** show your working outs.

INFORMATION FOR CANDIDATES

- The **total mark** for this paper is **100**.
- The marks for each question are shown on the **right** side of each page.
- Questions labelled with an asterisk (*) will assess the **quality** of **written communication**.

ADVICE FOR CANDIDATES

- Keep a close eye on the **time**.
- **Do not** spend too long on one question.
- Try to answer **every** question and show your workings out when required.

For examiner's use							
Q	Attempt No.			**Q**	Attempt No.		
	1	2	3		1	2	3
1				12			
2				13			
3				14			
4				15			
5				16			
6				17			
7				18			
8				19			
9				20			
10				21			
11				22			
TOTAL							

GCSE Mathematics
Foundation Tier
Formula Sheet

Area of trapezium $= \dfrac{1}{2}(a + b)h$

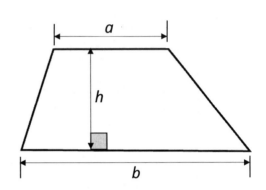

Volume of prism = area of cross-section x length

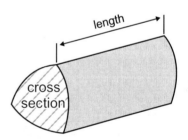

Answer ALL questions.
Write your answers in the spaces provided.

1 Collette has been studying Dance at GCSE level for one of her school subjects.

In order for Collette to pass the course, she must achieve at least 70% in each assessment in order to pass the whole course.

Individual Dance = Collette received 15 marks out of 20.

Group Dance = Collette received 20 marks out of 40.

Written Portfolio = Collette received 45 marks out of 60.

(a) Calculate the percentage for each part of her Dance assessment.

....

....

....

Individual Dance = ...%

Group Dance = ...%

Written Portfolio = ...%

(3 marks)

*(b) Explain whether or not Collette passed her Dance course.

....

....

....

(3 marks)

2 The diagram below contains lines of three numbers, each having a total of 15.

Complete the diagram using the numbers from 1 to 9. Each number can only be used **ONCE**.

We have provided you with the first three numbers.

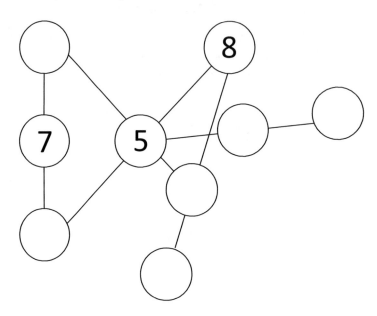

(4 marks)

3 Below is a set of numbers.

(a) Circle the THREE squared numbers.

| 17 | 45 | 49 | 12 | 64 | 91 | 50 | 4 | 5 | 18 | 30 | 15 |

(1 mark)

(b) Circle ALL of the factors of 90.

| 17 | 45 | 49 | 12 | 64 | 91 | 50 | 4 | 5 | 18 | 30 | 15 |

(1 mark)

(c) Circle ALL of the prime numbers.

| 17 | 45 | 49 | 12 | 64 | 91 | 50 | 4 | 5 | 18 | 30 | 15 |

(1 mark)

4 Here is a number machine.

Input   Output

(.......) ➡ [÷ 8] ➡ [x 9] ➡ (45)

(a) Work out the **input** when the output of the machine is 45.

....

....

....

Answer = ...

(1 mark)

Here is the same machine again.

Input   Output

(72) ➡ [÷ 8] ➡ [x 9] ➡ (.......)

(b) Work out the **output** when the input of the machine is 72.

....

....

....

Answer = ...

(1 mark)

Here is a different machine.

Input   Output

(150) ➡ [.......] ➡ [- 47] ➡ (553)

(c) Work out the **operation** that is missing from the machine.

....

....

....

Answer = ...

(1 mark)

5 Triangle ABC is a right angle.

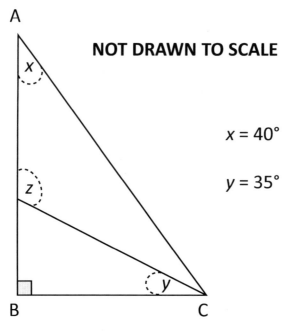

A

NOT DRAWN TO SCALE

$x = 40°$

$y = 35°$

B   C

(a) Work out the angle of **z**.

....

....

....

....

....

Answer = ...

(3 marks)

6 Below are eight shapes which are made by 1x1 squares.

Shape A   Shape B   Shape C   Shape D

Shape E   Shape F   Shape G   Shape H

(a) Which shape is a net for a cube?

Answer = ...

(1 mark)

(b) Which **two** shapes can be joined together to make a 4x4 square?

Answer = ...

(1 mark)

(c) Which shape contains one line of symmetry?

Answer = ...

(1 mark)

(d) What is the area of Shape F?

....

....

Answer = ...

(1 mark)

7 Work out the area of this parallelogram.

9 cm   8 cm   **NOT DRAWN TO SCALE**

17 cm

....

....

....

....

....

....

....

....

....

Answer = ...

(4 marks)

8 Below is a net of a cuboid.

The net shows the **area** of each face of the cuboid.

```
                    ┌─────────────┐
                    │             │
                    │   18 cm²    │
                    │             │
┌─────────────┬─────┼─────────────┼─────┐
│             │     │             │     │
│   27 cm²    │6 cm²│   27 cm²    │6 cm²│
│             │     │             │     │
└─────────────┴─────┼─────────────┼─────┘
                    │             │
                    │   18 cm²    │
                    │             │
                    └─────────────┘
```

Work out the volume of the cuboid.

....

....

....

....

....

....

....

Answer = ...

(5 marks)

9 Three people take part in a quiz.

There are 3 subject areas to the quiz: music, sport and general knowledge.

Each quiz is out of 50.

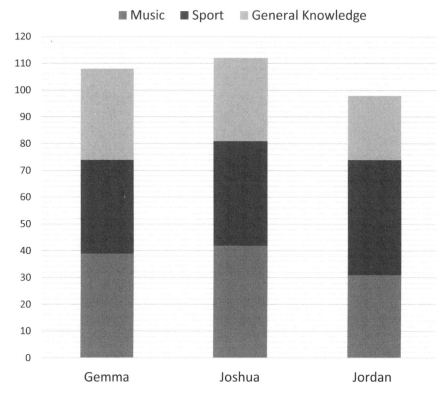

(a) Who scored the highest in the music section of the pop quiz?

Answer = ...

(1 mark)

(b) What was Gemma's average mark across all three subjects?

....

....

....

Answer = ...

(2 marks)

(c) What was each person's total score for the pop quiz?

....

....

....

....

Gemma = ...

Joshua = ...

Jordan = ...

(2 marks)

10 Here is a map of an island.

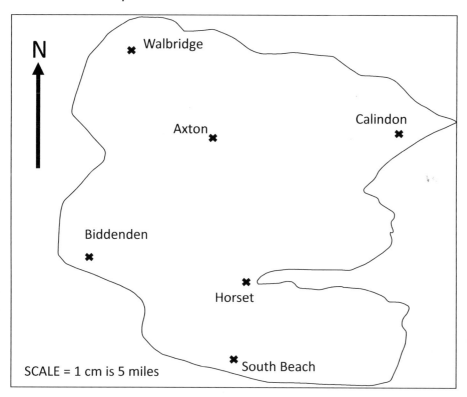

(a) Calculate how many miles it is from Walbridge to Horset. Use a straight line to connect both points.

....

....

....

Answer = ...

(2 marks)

(b) Write down the bearing from Calindon to Biddenden.

....

....

....

Answer = ...

(1 mark)

(c) Polly is going to university. She is moving out of her parents' house at South Beach and is going to a university in Axton.

She decides to drive. If 5 miles takes approximately 10 minutes, how long will it take Polly to get from South Beach to Axton?

....

....

....

Answer = ...

(2 marks)

11 Complete the table below. Write the fractions in their simplest form.

Fraction	Decimal	Percentage
$^4/_5$		
	0.35	
		1%

(3 marks)

12 A receptionist records the number of phone calls she has to take per day. Her results are recorded for 30 days.

Her results are recorded using the stem and leaf diagram below.

KEY: 1|1 represents 11 phone calls

0	3 3 4 6 6 7 7 9 9 9
1	0 1 1 2 2 2 4 7 8 8 8 9
2	0 0 2 2 4 5 6 6

(a) Work out the range.

....

Answer = ...

(1 mark)

(b) Work out the mean.

....

Answer = ...

(1 mark)

(c) Work out the median.

....

Answer = ...

(1 mark)

(d) Work out the mode.

....

Answer = ...

(1 mark)

(e) If the receptionist takes 17 phone calls in a day, and each call lasted approximately 8 minutes, how long did the receptionist spend taking calls that day? Write your answer in hours and minutes.

....

....

....

Answer = ...

(1 mark)

13 Below are three expressions.

$$ba \qquad \frac{b}{a} \qquad b-a$$

(a) (i) If $a = 4$ and $b = 24$, which of the following expressions has the smallest value?

....

....

....

      Answer = ...

(2 marks)

(ii) Work out $6y + 6x$, when $x = 3$ and $y = -2$

....

....

....

      Answer = ...

(2 marks)

(b) If $x^2 = 81$, the only value x can be is 9.

Is this true? Show your working out.

....

....

....

(1 mark)

14 Rachel and Joey are getting married.

They have £3,000 to spend on the evening food.

Below are the only two options available at such short notice.

| Option 1 | Option 2 |

Option 1

Evening buffet
throughout the night

£37.80 per guest

20% off whole price

Option 2

3 course meal

Up to 49 guests = £62.30
50 – 69 guests = £56.20
70 – 89 guests = £47.10
90+ guests = £41.30
Prices are per guest

Rachel and Joey have a total of 85 people attending the evening.

Explain why they **must** choose option 1.

....

....

....

....

....

....

....

....

....

(4 marks)

15 **(a)** (i) Work out the value of *x*.

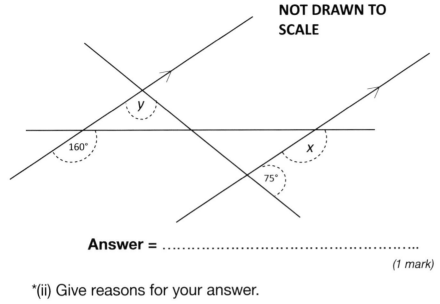

NOT DRAWN TO SCALE

Answer = ...

(1 mark)

*(ii) Give reasons for your answer.

....

....

....

(2 marks)

(b) Work out the value of *x*.

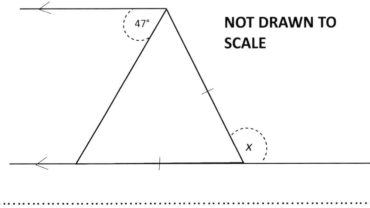

NOT DRAWN TO SCALE

....

....

....

Answer = ...

(2 marks)

16 A survey of 200 people show men and women's favourite type of TV programme.

	Soap	Drama	Sport	Reality TV	Documentary	Cooking	Game Show	Music	Animal	Other
Men	7	2	38	-	24	6	7	4	9	3
Women	23	34	4	17	4	5	3	9	1	-

(a) Draw a graph or chart displaying all of the data shown above.

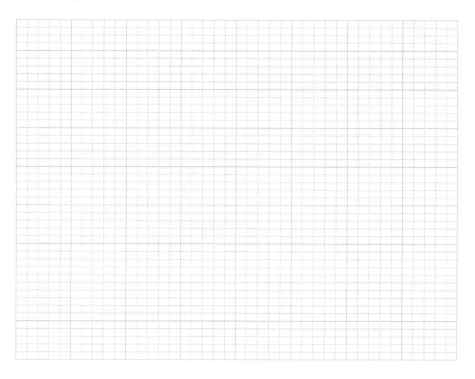

(5 marks)

17 Naveed is planning a surprise birthday party for his daughter. In total, there are 28 children attending and 12 adults.

Naveed is sorting out how much food and drink he will need to buy for the party. He is given a quote.

> ### SPECIAL OFFER
>
> Children's buffet = £6.30 per person
>
> Adult's buffet = £13.20 per person
>
> *(Drinks are included in the price).*

Work out how much it is going to cost Naveed to cover everyone's food and drink.

....

....

....

....

....

....

....

....

Answer = ...

(5 marks)

18 (a) Work out   0.6 x 0.2

Answer = ...
(1 mark)

(b) Work out $\dfrac{4}{6} \times \dfrac{5}{7}$. In its simplest form.

....

....

Answer = ...
(1 mark)

(c) Work out $\dfrac{2}{3} \div \dfrac{1}{4}$. Write your answer as a mixed fraction.

....

....

Answer = ...
(2 marks)

(d) Shanelle wants to buy a new car. She has £12,000 to spend on a new car including her first years' insurance plus car tax.

The car she is looking at is £9,975. The car insurance for the year is £1,480. The car tax is £120 for the year.

Can she afford the car? Show your working out.

....

....

....

....

(2 marks)

19 Write each of the following expressions in their simplest form.

(a) 8^0

Answer = ...

(1 mark)

(b) $9^9 \times 9^5$

Answer = ...

(1 mark)

(c) $7^8 \div 7^7$

Answer = ...

(1 mark)

(d) $13^9 \div 13^1$

Answer = ...

(1 mark)

(e) $y^{15} \times y^4$

Answer = ...

(1 mark)

20 A psychologist works on a fixed charge depending on the duration of each session.

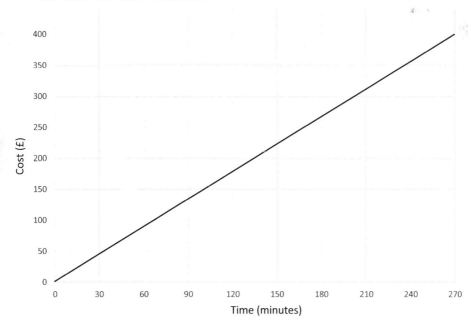

(a) How much does the psychologist charge for 15 minutes?

Answer = ...

(1 mark)

(b) How much does the psychologist charge for 1 hour and 30 minutes?

Answer = ...

(1 mark)

(c) If a client comes for a 90 minute session twice a week, for five weeks, how much will he have to pay?

....

....

....

Answer = ...

(2 marks)

(d) Simon says:

'It will be cheaper if I pay for two 30 minute sessions as opposed to paying for a single 1 hour session'.

Is Simon correct? Show your working out.

....

....

....

(1 mark)

(e) A different psychologist charges 20% more for a 1 hour session. How much does that psychologist charge?

....

....

....

Answer = ...

(1 mark)

21 Tony asked 200 adults which season they preferred: winter, spring, summer or autumn.

Of the 42 people who said their favourite season was winter, 34 of them were male.

½ of the total number of people surveyed said their favourite season was summer. 60% of which were female.

18 men and 15 women chose spring as their favourite season.

The rest of them said autumn. The men to women ratio who chose spring was 3 : 2.

Work out how many men and how many women chose autumn as their favourite season.

You will be awarded marks for workings out.

....

....

....

....

....

(3 marks)

Men = ...

Women = ...

(2 marks)

22 (a) Circle the correct equation that represents **line A**.

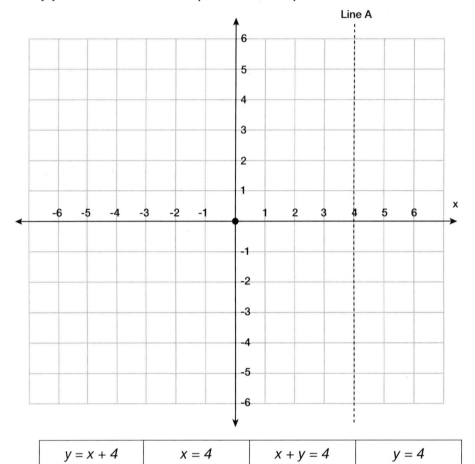

| $y = x + 4$ | $x = 4$ | $x + y = 4$ | $y = 4$ |

(2 marks)

(b) On the graph above, draw a line for: $x + y = 5$

(2 marks)

SURNAME		CENTRE NAME					
FIRST NAME/S		CENTRE NUMBER					
CANDIDATE SIGNATURE		CANDIDATE NUMBER					

GCSE Mathematics

SET B
Paper 2 Calculator

Foundation Tier

1 hour and 45 minutes

INSTRUCTIONS TO CANDIDATES

- Use **black** ink.

- **Fill in the boxes** at the top of this page.

- Answer **all** of the questions.

- **Clearly** show your working outs.

- Take the value of π to be 3.142, or use the button π on your calculator.

INFORMATION FOR CANDIDATES

- The **total mark** for this paper is **100**.

- The marks for each question are shown on the **right** side of each page.

- Questions labelled with an asterisk (*) will assess the **quality** of **written communication**.

ADVICE FOR CANDIDATES

- Keep a close eye on the **time**.

- **Do not** spend too long on one question.

- Try to answer **every** question and show your workings out when required.

For examiner's use							
Q	Attempt No.			**Q**	Attempt No.		
	1	2	3		1	2	3
1				12			
2				13			
3				14			
4				15			
5				16			
6				17			
7				18			
8				19			
9				20			
10				21			
11				22			
TOTAL							

Answer ALL questions.
Write your answers in the spaces provided.

1 The below table gives information about student grades for the academic year.

	A grade	B grade	C grade	D grade	Below a D grade	TOTAL
Year 9	17	34	81	53	34	219
Year 10	19	42	108	37	29	235
Year 11	8	27	149	42	21	247
Year 12	11	34	76	59	24	204

The head teacher wants to see whether or not the students met the target of achieving A-C grades. Across Year 10, the target was for 84% of pupils to achieve grades of A-C.

Was their target met?

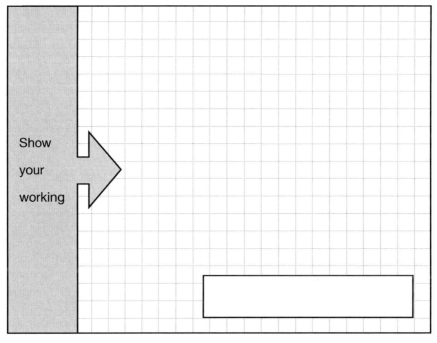

Show your working

(4 marks)

2 Angle **DEA** = 100°

Angle **BCD** = 35°

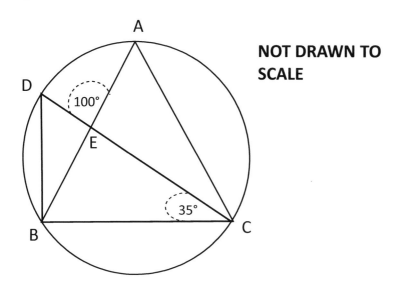

NOT DRAWN TO SCALE

Work out the angle = **BDC**.

You must show all of your working out.

....

....

....

....

....

....

....

....

....

(3 marks)

3   Below indicates the position of a tourist **A** in relation to the
    National History Museum, **M**.

    Tourist A is 27 kilometres away on the bearing 034° from the
    zoo, **Z**.

(a) Using the scale 1 cm = 9 km, draw on the diagram the
position of the zoo from where tourist **A** is standing. Mark the
position with a cross, and write the letter **Z**.

....

....

(2 marks)

(b) How far away is the tourist from the National History
Museum, **M**? To the nearest cm. Your answer should be in
kilometres.

....

....

(2 marks)

(c) From the National History Museum, **M**, plot the distance
45 kilometres, using the bearing 134°. *(1cm = 9 km)*

....

....

(2 marks)

4 A spinner has 10 equal sections.

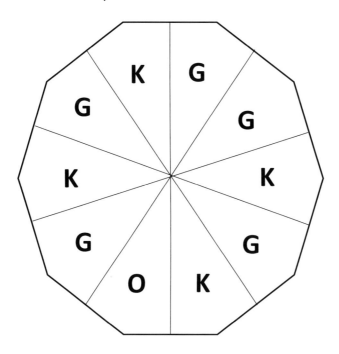

Mark each letter on the probability scale below. This needs to represent the probability of landing on that letter.

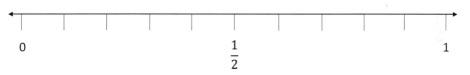

0                                      $\frac{1}{2}$ 1

(3 marks)

5 Below is a bar chart displaying heights of mountains.

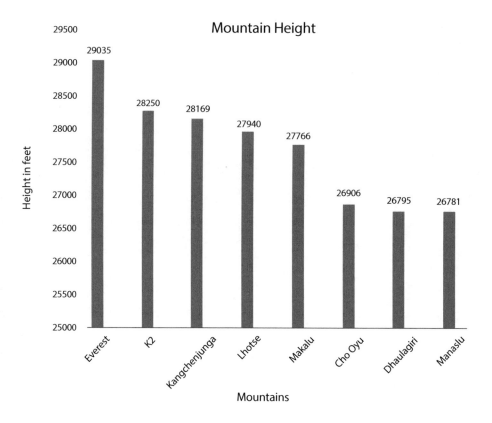

(a) Work out the average height, to the nearest hundred.

Answer = ...

(2 marks)

(b) What is the range between the highest mountain and the smallest mountain?

Answer = ...

(2 marks)

6 The width of the rectangle is 100 metres. The length of the rectangle is 240 metres.

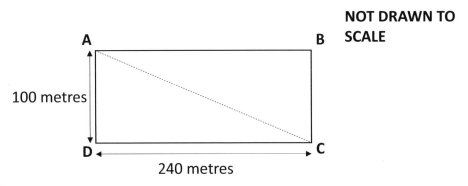

NOT DRAWN TO SCALE

To make sure that the angles of the rectangle are exactly 90°, work out the distance of the diagonal *AC*.

....

....

....

....

....

....

....

Answer = ...

(4 marks)

7 **(a)** On the grid, reflect shape A using the line $y = x$.

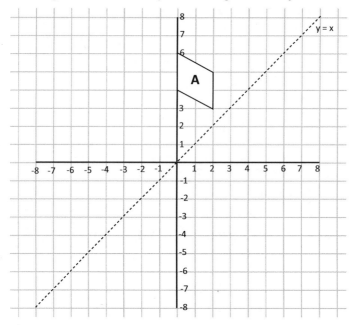

(2 marks)

(b) On the grid, rotate shape A 90° clockwise, using the coordinates (-1, 0).

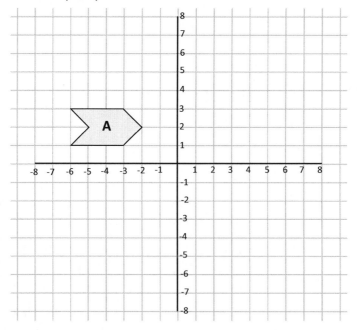

(2 marks)

8 Using trial and improvement, solve the equation $x^2 + 2x = 40$, correct to 1 decimal place.

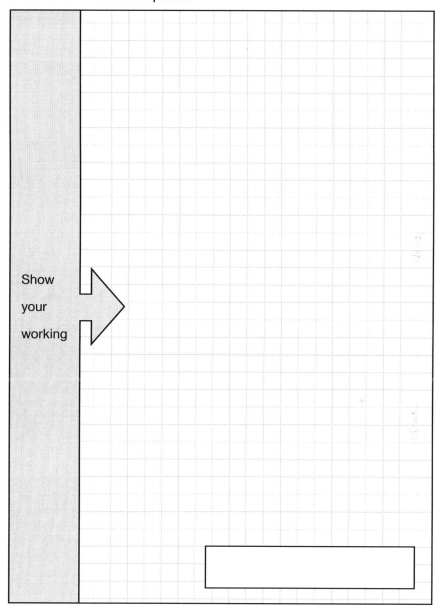

Show your working

(3 marks)

9 **(a)** (i) Simplify the following expression:

$5y + 6y - 3 - 4y + 8$

Answer = ...

(ii) Simplify the following expression:

$3x^2 + 11x + 4 - 3x + 7$

Answer = ...

(1 mark)

(b) (i) Solve the following equation:

$3q + 9 = 21$

Answer = ...

(1 mark)

(ii) Solve the following equation:

$4(3x + 15) = 3(5x + 17.5)$

....

....

....

Answer = ...

(2 marks)

10 Harrison, Katie and Ryan all work in a restaurant during their summer holidays.

In total, they earn £780 in tips in just 6 weeks.

They decide to split the money in the ratio of the number of hours each person worked. The ratio they split these tips into is 12 : 8 : 20.

(a) Calculate how much each person will receive in tips.

....

....

....

Harrison = ...

Katie = ...

Ryan = ...

(3 marks)

(b) Write the above ratio in its simplest form.

Answer = ...

(1 mark)

(c) In total, how much do Harrison, Katie and Ryan make per week?

....

....

Answer = ...

(1 mark)

11 The two-way table below compares pupils' results for GCSE English with GCSE Media grades.

English GCSE Grades	A*	A	B	C	D	E	F	U	Total
A*									
A		2	2	3					7
B		1	3	4				1	9
C			8	10	6	1			25
D				1		2			3
E								1	1
F									
U									
Total		3	13	18	6	3		2	45

Media GCSE Grades (column headers A* through U)

(a) How many pupils achieved a C grade in Media and an A grade in English?

Answer = ...

(1 mark)

(b) What percentage of the total pupils achieved a C grade in Media?

Answer = ...

(1 mark)

(c) How many pupils achieved a C grade or above in Media?

Answer = ...

(1 mark)

(d) If 8 people achieved a C grade in English, what was their Media score?

Answer = ...

(1 mark)

(e) What subject scored the highest number of A-C grades?

Answer = ...

(1 mark)

12 Below is a bar chart displaying the consumption of petrol across different countries. These totals have been rounded up to the nearest million.

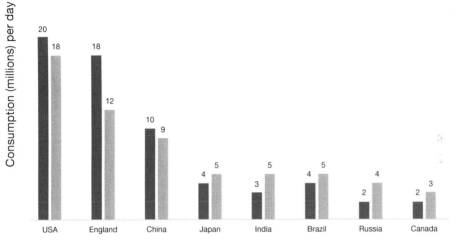

Consumption of Petrol

■ 2014 Petrol Consumption ▨ 2013 Petrol Consumption

(a) In England, if the petrol consumption dropped by 8% from 2014 to 2015, how much would England's petrol consumption be in 2015?

....

....

Answer = ...

(2 marks)

(b) What was the difference in petrol consumption for the USA from 2013 to 2014?

....

....

Answer = ...

(2 marks)

13 (a) Work out the missing measurement on the triangle below. Write your answer to 2 decimal places.

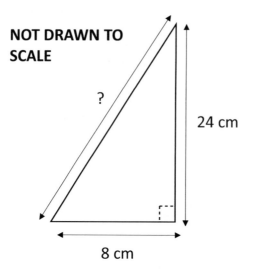

NOT DRAWN TO SCALE

?

24 cm

8 cm

....

....

....

Answer = ...

(3 marks)

(b) Work out the missing measurement on the triangle below. Write your answer to one decimal place.

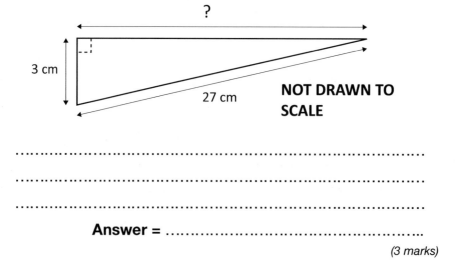

?

3 cm

27 cm

NOT DRAWN TO SCALE

....

....

....

Answer = ...

(3 marks)

14 Millie and her friend Sarah are playing with a frisbee.

Millie throws the frisbee 30 metres at a rate of 12 m/s.

Sarah spends 4 seconds to walk and pick up the frisbee.

Millie runs back to Sarah at a constant speed of 6 m/s.

Draw a distance and time graph to show the above information.

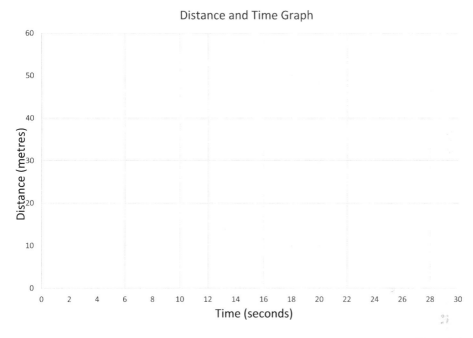

Distance and Time Graph

(4 marks)

15 Megan needs to work out an area of a field in hectares.

She knows that 1 hectare = 10,000m²

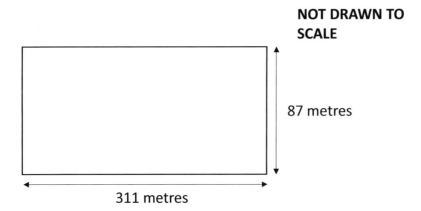

NOT DRAWN TO SCALE

87 metres

311 metres

Using the above information, calculate the area of the field (in hectares). Your answer **must** be written to 1 decimal place.

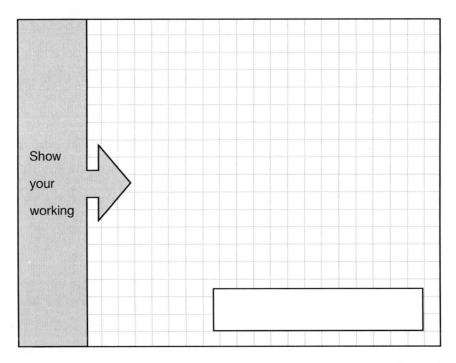

Show your working

(3 marks)

16 Use trial and improvement to solve the equation $x^3 - 3x = 36$.

Your answer should be correct to 1 decimal place.

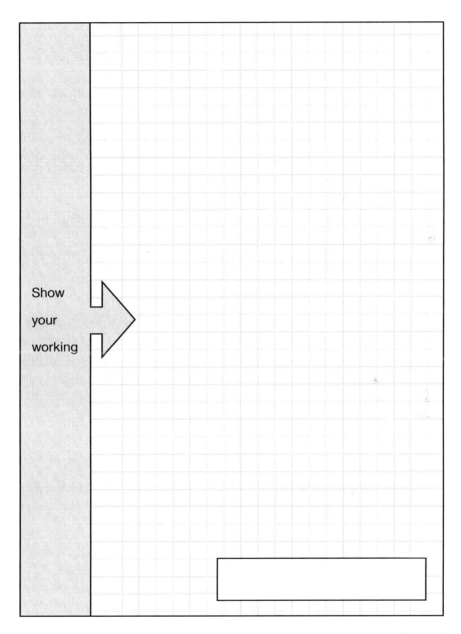

Show your working

(5 marks)

17 (a) If $a = 4b + 9c$, work out the value of a when $b = 17$ and $c = 12$.

....

....

Answer = ...

(2 marks)

(b) Factorise $4x + 16$

....

....

Answer = ...

(1 mark)

(c) Expand and simplify $10(y + 2) + 2(y + 6)$

....

....

Answer = ...

(2 marks)

18 Ollie and David are going on holiday.

They need to change their British pounds into dollars.

(a) They have £1,340 to change into dollars with the exchange rate of £1 = $1.36.

Work out how many whole dollars they will have.

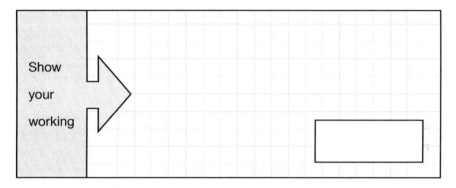

(3 marks)

(b) Once they arrive at their destination, Ollie buys a new pair of trainers costing $85.

Using the exchange rate of £1 = $1.36, work out how much the pair of trainers would have cost in pound sterling.

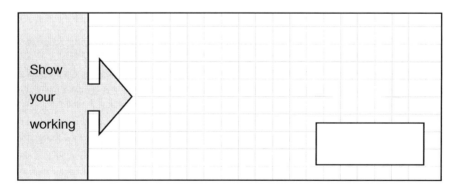

(3 marks)

19 (a) Given that $\dfrac{48 \times 6.5}{78} = 4$

Work out the value of $\dfrac{4.8 \times 65}{7.8}$

....

....

Answer = ...

(2 marks)

(b) Use your calculator to work out $78.8 - \sqrt{784}$

....

....

Answer = ...

(1 mark)

(c) Calculate the exact value of $4.4^3 - 1.4^4$

....

....

Answer = ...

(2 marks)

20 Here are the times, *in minutes*, of how long Sally takes her dog out for a walk each day.

23 35 38 15 25 21 20 26 39 34 23 18 16 14 18

(a) Calculate the mean time Sally spends walking her dog, to 1 decimal place.

....

....

Answer = ...

(1 mark)

(b) Write the above information using the frequency table below.

Time	Tally	Frequency
0-10		
11-20		
21-30		
31-40		

(2 marks)

(c) Using your frequency table, draw a bar chart to represent the same information. Remember to label the bars on the Time axis.

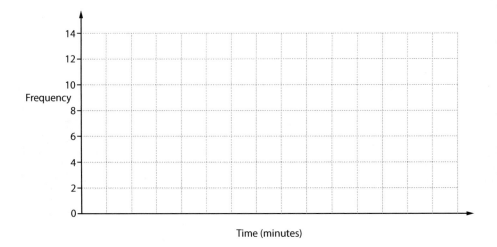

(2 marks)

21 Study the following chart and answer the four questions that follow.

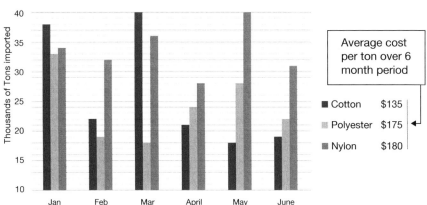

(a) What is the mean value for nylon imported over the 6 month period?

....

....

Answer = ...

(2 marks)

(b) What is the range for polyester imports across the 6 month period?

....

....

Answer = ...

(2 marks)

(c) What was the difference in thousands of tons between cotton material and nylon material imports across the first 3 months of the year?

....

....

Answer = ...

(2 marks)

22 Below shows four different companies with key information.

Company	Company Profit (Annual) (£)	Cost to buy company (£)	Number of employees
A	15,000	18,000	6
B	26,000	24,000	11
C	22,000	20,000	8
D	40,000	40,000	10

(a) How much profit did Company C make in the year?

....

....

Answer = ...

(1 mark)

(b) On average, how much did Company D make per month, based on the annual profit? To the nearest whole number.

....

....

Answer = ...

(1 mark)

(c) How much more did Company D make than Company B?

....

....

Answer = ...

(1 mark)

(d) If company A makes an increased profit of 8% in the following year, how much do they make in the following year?

....

....

Answer = ...

(2 marks)

GCSE

Mathematics

SET B

Calculator and Non-Calculator Paper

Foundation Tier

ANSWER BOOKLET

SET B – PAPER 1
(Non-Calculator)

1. (a) Individual dance = 75%	3 marks
Group dance = 50%	(1 mark for each correct answer).
Written Portfolio = 75%	
1. (b) No, she only scored 50% in the group dance, and she needed 70% in each assessment in order to pass the whole course.	3 marks
	(2 marks for correct explanation).
	(1 mark for quality of written communication).
2. Your answer should look like this:	4 marks
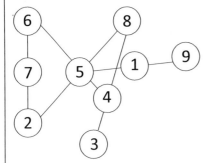	(Award all 4 marks for all correct answers. Deduct 1 mark for any line that doesn't add up to 15).
3. (a) 49, 64 and 4	1 mark
2 x 2 = 4	(Award 1 mark for all correct answers).
7 x 7 = 49	
8 x 8 = 64	
3. (b) 45, 5, 18, 30, 15	1 mark
The factors of 90 are:	(Only award 1 mark for all correct answers).
1 and 90;	
2 and 45;	
3 and 30;	
5 and 18;	
6 and 15;	
9 and 10.	

3. (c) 17 and 5

Prime numbers are numbers that can only be divided by itself and one:

1 x 17 = 17 (no other numbers can be divided into 17).

1 x 5 = 5 (no other numbers can be divided into 5).

1 mark

(Only award 1 mark for both correct answers).

4. (a) 40

To work out the input, you need to work backwards starting with the output. In order to work backwards, you must do the opposite to what the operation is saying.

45 ÷ 9 = 5

5 x 8 = 40

So, 40 ÷ 8 = 5.   5 x 9 = 45

1 mark

4. (b) 81

72 ÷ 8 = 9

9 x 9 = 81

1 mark

4. (c) x4 or +450

553 + 47 = 600

600 ÷ 4 = 150

So, 150 x 4 = 600 − 47 = 553

or

150 + 450 = 600 − 47 = 553

1 mark

5. (a) 125°

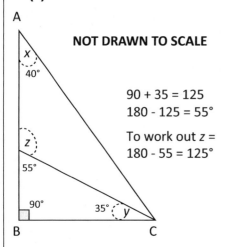

A

NOT DRAWN TO SCALE

x

40°

$90 + 35 = 125$
$180 - 125 = 55°$

To work out $z =$
$180 - 55 = 125°$

z

55°

90°

35° y

B

C

3 marks

(1 mark for correct answer).

(1 mark for working out the angles in a triangle, and the angles in a straight line).

(1 mark for showing working out).

6. (a) Shape F

A cube has 6 faces, therefore this rules out shapes A, B, C, D, G and H.

Shape E does not make up a cube.

1 mark

6. (b) Shapes D and E

If you joined shapes D and E, this would make a 4 x 4 square.

1 mark

6. (c) Shape G

Only shape G has one line of symmetry.

1 mark

6. (d) 6 cm²

The shape is built up of 1 x 1 squares. There are 6 squares in total, therefore the area is 6 cm².

1 mark

7.   136 cm²

Area of a parallelogram = base x height

   8 x 17 = 136

4 marks

(Award 1 mark for correct answer).

(Award 1 mark for correct formula).

(Award 2 marks for showing calculations. Award 1 mark only if an error occurs in the calculation).

8.   54 cm³

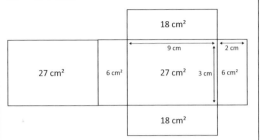

Volume = height x width x length

2 x 9 x 3 = 54

5 marks

(Award 1 mark for correct answer).

(Award 2 marks for working out the correct height and width of each side face).

(Award 2 marks for showing workings out).

9. (a) Joshua

Joshua scored 42 marks in the music quiz. This was the highest score for music, therefore Joshua scored the highest.

1 mark

9. (b) 36

Gemma scored 39 out of 50, 35 out of 50 and 34 out of 50.

Her mean mark is:

39 + 35 + 34 = 108

108 ÷ 3 = 36

2 marks

(1 mark for adding up Gemma's correct marks for each subject).

(1 mark adding them up and dividing it by the number of subjects (3)).

9. (c) Gemma = 39 + 35 + 34 = 108

Joshua = 42 + 39 + 31 = 112

Jordan = 31 + 43 + 24 = 98

Remember, each person's total cannot be read by the height of the bar. The bar is broken up into three sections, and each of these sections would need to begin from 0, not the number it starts with on line of the chart.

2 marks

(2 marks for all correct answers. 1 mark for no more than one error).

10. (a) 35 miles

Measured in cm between Walbridge and Horset, is 7 cm.

7 x 5 = 35 miles

2 marks

(1 mark for correct answer).

(1 mark for showing working out).

10. (b) 249°

1 mark

10. (c) 1 hour

2 marks

Between South Beach and Axton is 6 cm.

(1 mark for correct answer).

$$6 \times 5 = 30 \text{ miles}$$

(1 mark for showing working out).

If 5 miles takes 10 minutes, 30 miles will take 60 minutes (1 hour).

11. Your answer should look like this:

Fraction	Decimal	Percentage
$\frac{4}{5}$	0.8	80%
$\frac{7}{20}$	0.35	35%
$\frac{1}{100}$	0.01	1%

3 marks

(1 mark for each correct row).

12. (a) 23

To work out the range, you need to subtract the lowest number (3) from the highest number (26)

1 mark

$$26 - 3 = 23$$

12. (b) 14

To work out the mean, you need to add up all of the totals, and then divide it by how many numbers there are:

1 mark

Row 1 = 3 + 3 + 4 + 6 + 6 + 7 + 7 + 9 + 9 + 9 = 63

Row 2 = 10 + 11 + 11 + 12 + 12 + 12 + 14 + 17 + 18 + 18 + 18 + 19 = 172

Row 3 = 20 + 20 + 22 + 22 + 24 + 25 + 26 + 26 = 185

$$63 + 172 + 185 = 420$$

$$420 \div 30 = 14$$

12. (c) 12   1 mark

To work out the median, you need to work out which number is in the middle. There are 30 numbers which mean two numbers will be in the middle.

The numbers 12 + 12 are both in the middle, therefore 12 is the middle (median) number.

12. (d) 9, 12 and 18   1 mark

To work out the mode, you need to see which number occurs the most.

9, 12 and 18 all occur three times, and therefore all three of these are the mode for this set of data.

12. (e) 2 hours and 16 minutes   1 mark

If the receptionist took 17 calls, and each call lasted approximately 8 minutes, the time spent on the phone is:

$17 \times 8 = 136.$

The question asks for the answer in hours and minutes, so you need to convert 136 minutes into hours and minutes. (60 minutes are in 1 hour).

136 minutes = 2 hours and 16 minutes

13. (a) (i) b/a   2 marks

b/a is the smallest in value.   (1 mark for correct answer).

$ba = b \times a = 24 \times 4 = 96$ (1 mark for showing working out).

$b/a = b \div a = 24 \div 4 = 6$

$b - a = 24 - 4 = 20$

13. (a) (ii) 6

$6y = 6 \times -2 = -12$

$6x = 6 \times 3 = 18$

$-12 + 18 = 6$

2 marks

(1 mark for correct answer).

(1 mark for showing working out).

13. (b) Yes, 9 can be the only number to replace the x in the expression x^2.

If $x^2 = 81$, that means you need to find the square root of 81, which is 9.

1 mark

(1 mark for saying it is true and explaining why. Must refer to square root).

14. Option 2 is not an option for Joey and Rachel because it is out of their price range:

Option 1 = 37.80 x 85 = 3213

20% off whole price = 642.60

3213 – 642.60 = £2570.40

Option 2 = 47.10 x 85 = 4003.5

4 marks

(2 marks for explaining the price for option 1).

(2 marks for explaining the price for option 2).

15. (a) (i) 160°

1 mark

15. (a) (ii) Angle x is on parallel lines with the angle marked 160°. Therefore these angles will be the same.

2 marks

(1 mark for correct answer).

(1 mark for quality of written communication).

15. (b) 94°

Opposite angles (indicated by the dotted line) are the same.

The isosceles triangle (indicated by the dashes on two of the lines) means that the two angles are the same.

Therefore $180 – 47 – 47 = 86°$.

$180 – 86 = 94°$.

2 marks

(1 mark for correct answer).

(1 mark for explaining how opposite angles have the same angle, and how isosceles triangles have two angles of the same value).

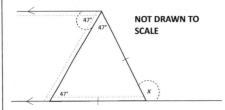

47° 47°

NOT DRAWN TO SCALE

47°

x

16. (a) A graph that allows you to compare two sets of data (men and women), would work sufficiently.

A great chart to demonstrate this would be a comparative bar chart.

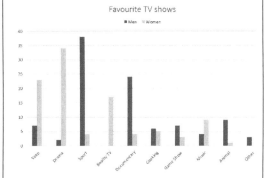

5 marks

(1 mark for choosing a chart that conveys all of the data in a clear manner).

(3 marks for filling in the chart correctly).

(1 mark for using labels and titling the chart).

17. £334.80

Children = 6.30 x 28 = £176.40

Adults = 13.20 x 12 = £158.40

176.40 + 158.40 = £334.80

5 marks

(1 mark for correct answer).

(2 marks for working out children cost).

(2 marks for working out adult cost).

18. (a) 0.12

The best thing to do is remove the decimal points, do the calculation, and then add in the decimal points at the end.

So, 6 x 2 = 12.

There are 2 numbers after the decimal points in the question (one after .6 and one after .2). Therefore two numbers have to come after the decimal point in the answer 12 = 0.12

1 mark

18. (b) 10/21

$$\frac{4}{6} \times \frac{5}{7} = \frac{20}{42} = \frac{10}{21}$$

1 mark

18. (c) 2 2/3

$$\frac{2}{3} \div \frac{1}{4}$$

$$\frac{2}{3} \times \frac{4}{1} = \frac{8}{3} = 2\frac{2}{3}$$

2 marks

(1 mark for improper fraction).

(1 mark for converting the answer to a mixed fraction).

18. (d) Yes, she can afford the car

The cost of the car = £9,975

The cost of her car tax for the year = £120

The cost of 1 years' insurance = £1,480

So, 9,975 + 1,480 + 120 = 11,575

Shanelle has £12,000 to spend. Therefore she can afford to buy the car.

2 marks

(1 mark for correct answer).

(1 mark for showing workings out).

19. (a) 1

1 mark

19. (b) 9^{14}

$9^9 \times 9^5 = 9^{9+5}$

1 mark

19. (c) 7^1

$7^8 \div 7^7 = 7^{8-7}$

1 mark

19. (d) 13^8

$13^9 \div 13^1 = 13^{9-1}$

1 mark

19. (e) y^{19}

$y^{15} \times y^4 = y^{15+4}$

1 mark

20. (a) £25

Using the graph, you need to find the 15 minutes along the bottom of the graph (because the graph goes up in 30 minutes, you need to find half of this). Work your way up until you reach the black line, and then work out the cost.

1 mark

20. (b) £135 *Read the number from the bottom of the graph which is equivalent to 1 hour and 30 minutes (90 minutes) and then work out how much that costs.*	1 mark
20. (c) £1,350 *£135 x 2 (number of times a week) = £270* *£270 x 5 (five weeks) = £1,350*	2 marks (1 mark for correct answer). (1 mark for showing working out).
20. (d) It would cost exactly the same if you paid for two 30 minute sessions, as opposed to paying for a single one hour session. *Paying for two 30 minute sessions = £45 x 2 = £90.* *Paying for a single one hour session = 90*	1 mark
20. (e) £108 *Cost for 1 hour = £90* *Another psychologist charges 20% more = 90 ÷ 100 x 20 = 18* *90 + 18 = £108*	1 mark
21. Men = 15 chose autumn as their favourite season **Women = 10 chose autumn as their favourite season** *200 – 42 (people who chose winter) = 158* *158 – 100 (people who chose summer) = 58* *58 – 18 – 15 (people who chose spring) = 25*	5 marks (1 mark for correct answer). (4 marks for showing working out. Deduct one mark for each error in calculations).

The ratio is 3 : 2 = 3 + 5

    25 ÷ 5 = 5

    5 x 3 = 15 (men who chose autumn)

    5 x 2 = 10 (women who chose autumn)

22. (a) y = 4   2 marks

The line is vertical which means it is using the y axis. It touches the x axis at point 4: y = 4

22. (b) Your answer should look like this: 2 marks

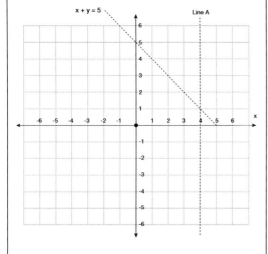

SET B – PAPER 2
(Calculator)

1. No, their target was not met

The number of Year 10 pupils who achieved an A-C grade was:

$$19 + 42 + 108 = 169$$

The total number of pupils in Year 10 = 235. So the percentage of pupils who achieved an A-C grade in Year 10:

$$169 \div 235 \times 100(\%) = 71.914...\%$$

Their target was 84%, and therefore this was not met.

4 marks

(1 mark for correct answer).

(3 marks for explanation. 1 mark for adding up the number of A-C grades from Year 10. 1 mark for dividing it by the total number of Year 10 pupils. 1 mark for multiplying this by 100%).

2. Angle BDC = 55°

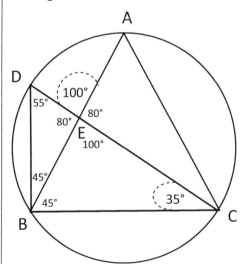

3 marks

(1 mark for correct answer).

(1 mark for working out angles on a straight line).

(1 mark for working out angles in a triangle).

3. (a) From Point A, you need to use a protractor and work out 034°. This should be plotted 3 cm away from point A (27 ÷ 9 = 3)

2 marks

(1 mark for correct answer).

(1 mark for labelling the cross with correct letter).

3. (b) 63 miles   2 marks

    7 x 9 = 63

3. (c) Your answer should be   2 marks
plotted 5 cm away. This should be
on the bearing of 134°.   (1 mark for correct answer).

(1 mark for correct attempt of the
following the right bearing).

4. Your answer should look like   3 marks
this:
(1 mark for correct placing of each
letter).

5. (a) 27,700   2 marks

        29035   (1 mark for correct answer).
        28250   (1 mark for showing workings out).
        28169
        27940
        27766
        26906
        26795
  +   26781
      221642

221642 ÷ 8(mountains) =
27,705.25

To the nearest hundred = 27,700

5. (b) 2,254   2 marks

Highest mountain = 29,035   (1 mark for correct answer).

Smallest mountain = 26,781   (1 mark for showing workings out).

    Range = 29,035 – 26,781 = 2,254

6. Diagonal = 260 metres

$$Diagonal = \sqrt{width^2 + length^2}$$

$$Diagonal = \sqrt{100^2 + 240^2}$$

$$Diagonal = \sqrt{10{,}000 + 57{,}600}$$

$$Diagonal = \sqrt{67{,}600}$$

$$= 260\ metres$$

4 marks

(1 mark for correct answer).

(1 mark for working out width^2).

(1 mark for working out length^2).

(1 mark for working out square root).

7. (a) Your answer should look like this:

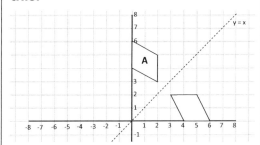

2 marks

7. (b) Your answer should look like this:

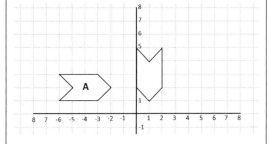

2 marks

8. x = 5.4

Let's start with y = 5

5 x 5 = 25

2 x 5 = 10

25 + 10 = 35 **TOO SMALL**

Let's try with y = 6

6 x 6 = 36

2 x 6 = 12

36 + 12 = 48 **TOO BIG**

Let's try with y = 5.5

5.5 x 5.5 = 30.25

2 x 5.5 = 11

30.25 + 11 = 41.25 **TOO BIG**

Let's try with y = 5.4

5.4 x 5.4 = 29.16

2 x 5.4 = 10.8

29.16 + 10.8 = 39.96 **CLOSE**

Therefore correct to 1 decimal place = 5.4

3 marks

(1 mark for correct answer).

(1 mark for rounding the number correct to 1 decimal place).

(1 mark for showing workings out).

9. (a) (i) 7y + 5

(5y) (+ 6y) (− 3) (− 4y) (+ 8)

(5y) (+ 6y) (- 4y) = 7y

(- 3) (+ 8) = + 5

7y + 5

1 mark

9. (a) (ii) 3x² + 8x + 11

(3x²) (+ 11x) (+ 4) (- 3x) (+ 7)

(3x²)

(+ 11x) (- 3x) = + 8x

(+ 4) (+ 7) = + 11

3x² + 8x + 11

1 mark

9. (b) (i) q = 4

21 – 9 = 12

(3 x ? = 12)

(3 x 4 = 12)

(3 x 4) + 9 = 21

q = 4

1 mark

9. (b) (ii) 2.5

4 (3x + 15) = 3 (5x + 17.5)

12x + 60 = 15x + 52.5

15x - 12x = 3x

60 - 52.5 = 7.5

3x = 7.5

x = 2.5

2 marks

(1 mark for correct answer).

(1 mark for showing workings out).

10. (a) Harrison = £234

     Katie = £156

     Ryan = £390

12 : 8 : 20 = 12 + 8 + 20 = 40

£780 ÷ 40 = 19.5

19.5 x 12 = £234 (Harrison)

19.5 x 8 = £156 (Katie)

19.5 x 20 = £390 (Ryan)

3 marks

(1 mark for each correct answer).

10. (b) 3 : 2 : 5

12 : 8 : 20

All of these numbers can be divided by 4.

12 ÷ 4 = 3

8 ÷ 4 = 2

20 ÷ 4 = 5

3 : 2 : 5

1 mark

10. (c) £130	1 mark
$£780 \div 6$ *(weeks) = £130*	
They make £130, on average, per week.	
11. (a) 3	1 mark
3 people achieved a C grade in Media AND an A grade in English.	
11. (b) 40%	1 mark
$18 \div 45 = 0.4$	
$0.4 \times 100 = 40\%$	
11. (c) 34	1 mark
$18 + 13 + 3 = 34$	
11. (d) B grade	1 mark
If 8 people achieved a C grade in English, their Media grade was a B.	
11. (e) English	1 mark
English A-C grades = 7 + 9 + 25 = 41	
Media A-C grades = 3 + 13 + 18 = 34	
English scored the best A-C grades.	
12. (a) 16.56 million per day	2 marks
$18 \div 100 = 0.18$	(1 mark for correct answer).
$0.18 \times 92 = 16.56\%$	(1 mark for showing workings out).
This is an 8% decrease from 2014 to 2015.	
12. (b) 2 million	2 marks
$20 - 18 = 2$ *(million)*	(1 mark for correct answer).
	(1 mark for showing workings out).

13. (a) 25.30 cm

Using Pythagoras' theorem:

$AB^2 + BC^2 = AC^2$
$AC^2 = 8^2 + 24^2$
$\quad = 64 + 576$
$\quad = 640$
$\quad = \sqrt{640}$
$\quad = 25.298...$

To 2 decimal places = 25.30 cm

3 marks

(1 mark for correct answer).

(1 mark for displaying Pythagoras' theorem).

(1 mark for showing all workings out with no more than one error).

13. (b) 7.7 cm

Using Pythagoras' theorem:

$AB^2 + 14^2 = 16^2$
$AB^2 + 196 = 256$
$256 - 196 = 60$
$AB^2 = 60$
$AB^2 = \sqrt{60}$
$\quad = 7.7459...$

To 1 decimal place = 7.7 cm

3 marks

(1 mark for correct answer).

(1 mark for displaying Pythagoras' theorem).

(1 mark for showing all workings out with no more than one error).

14. Your answer should look like this:

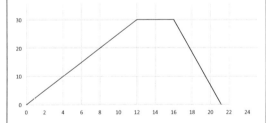

Millie throws the frisbee 30 metres at 12 m/s.

It takes 4 m/s to retrieve the frisbee.

Millie runs back to Sarah at a rate of 6 m/s.

Distance = speed ÷ time

30 (distance) ÷ 6 (speed) = 5 (time)

4 marks

(3 marks for showing correct data of throwing the frisbee, retrieving the frisbee, and throwing the frisbee back).

(1 mark for joining the points up using a straight line).

15. Hectares = 2.7

The area of the rectangle:

$87 \times 311 = 27,057$

10,000 metres in 1 hectare:

$27,057 \div 10,000 = 2.7057$

To 1 decimal place = 2.7 hectares.

3 marks

(1 mark for correct answer).

(1 mark for working out the area of the rectangle).

(1 mark for dividing the total by 10,000).

16. 3.6

Let's start with $x = 3$

$3^3 = 27$

$3 \times 3 = 9$

$27 - 9 = 18$ **TOO SMALL**

Let's try with $x = 4$

$4^3 = 64$

$4 \times 3 = 12$

$64 - 12 = 52$ **TOO BIG**

Let's try with $x = 3.5$

$3.5^3 = 42.875$

$3.5 \times 3 = 10.5$

$42.875 - 10.5 = 32.375$ **TOO SMALL**

Let's try with $x = 3.6$

$3.6^3 = 46.656$

$3.6 \times 3 = 10.8$

$46.656 - 10.8 = 35.856$ **CLOSE**

To the nearest whole number = 36

5 marks

(2 marks for correct answer).

(3 marks for showing workings out).

17. (a) a = 176

$a = (4 \times 17) + (9 \times 12)$

$a = (68) + (108)$

$a = 176$

2 marks

(1 mark for correct answer).

(1 mark for showing workings out).

17. (b) 4 (x + 4)

You need to find the largest factor that both the numbers go into (in this case both 4 and 16 have the common factor of 4).

1 mark

17. (c) 12y + 24

    10 (y + 2) + 2 (y + 6)

    10y + 12 + 2y + 12

    10y + 2y = 12y

    +12 + 12 = +24

    12y + 24

2 marks

(1 mark for correct answer).

(1 mark for showing workings out).

18. (a) $1822

    £1340 x 1.36 = 1822.4

The amount of whole dollars they have is $1822

3 marks

(1 mark for reaching the correct answer; without writing the answer in exact dollars).

(1 mark for writing the answer exactly).

(1 mark for showing workings out).

18. (b) £62.50

$85 ÷ 1.36 = 62.5

3 marks

(1 mark for correct answer).

(1 mark for showing workings out).

(1 mark for dividing by the exchange rate of pounds to dollars).

19. (a) 40

4.8 x 65 = 312

312 ÷ 7.8 = 40

2 marks

19. (b) 50.8

$\sqrt{784} = 28$

$78.8 - 28 = 50.8$

1 mark

19. (c) 81.3424

$4.4^3 = 85.184$

$1.4^4 = 3.8416$

$85.184 - 3.8416 = 81.3424$

2 marks

(1 mark for correct answer).

(1 mark for showing workings out).

20. (a) 24.3 minutes

$23 + 35 + 38 + 15 + 25 + 21 + 20 + 26 + 39 + 34 + 23 + 18 + 16 + 14 + 18 = 365$

$365 \div 15 = 24.333...$

To 1 decimal place = 24.3

1 mark

20. (b) Your answer should look like this:

Time	Tally	Frequency
0-10		
11-20	Жℐℐℐℐ	6
21-30	Жℐℐℐ	5
31-40	ℐℐℐℐ	4

2 marks

20. (c) Your answer should look something like this:

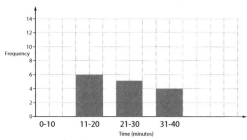

2 marks

(1 mark for correct answer).

(1 mark for correct bars on the chart, including labels of each bar. No marks to be awarded if the bar chart is missing labels).

21. (a) 33.5

To work out the mean: add the totals up and divide by how many numbers there are:

$34 + 32 + 36 + 28 + 40 + 31 = 201$

$201 \div 6 \text{ (months)} = 33.5$

2 marks

(1 mark for correct answer).

(1 mark for showing the correct method to work out the mean).

21. (b) 15

To work out the range:

    Highest polyester = 33

    Lowest polyester = 18

    33 – 18 = 15

2 marks

(1 mark for correct answer).

(1 mark for showing the correct method to work out the range).

21. (c) 2 thousand (tons)

Cotton material in first 3 months:

    38 + 22 + 40 = 100

Nylon material in first 3 months:

    34 + 32 + 36 = 102

2 marks

(1 mark for correct answer).

(1 mark for showing the correct method to work out the range).

22. (a) £22,000

Company C made an annual profit of £22,000.

1 mark

22. (b) £3,333

    40,000 ÷ 12 = 3333.333…

To the nearest whole number = £3333

1 mark

22. (c) £14,000

    Company D = £40,000

    Company B = £26,000

    40,000 – 26,000 = 14,000

1 mark

22. (d) £16,200

    15,000 ÷ 100 = 150

    150 x 108 = 16,200

2 marks

(1 mark for correct answer).

(1 mark for showing workings out).

NEED A LITTLE EXTRA HELP WITH GCSE MATHS?

GCSE Maths Is Easy is the ULTIMATE guide for anyone who finds mathematics challenging, and for anyone who wants to pass their GCSE maths exams with ease.

This exciting guide is filled with interesting facts and practice questions. With our help, you can learn to understand GCSE maths in a fun and compelling way!

FOR MORE INFORMATION ON OUR GCSE MATHS IS EASY GUIDE, PLEASE VISIT

WWW.HOW2BECOME.COM

Get Access To

FREE

Psychometric
Tests

www.PsychometricTestsOnline.co.uk